STATISTICS FOR EDUCATION
AND PHYSICAL EDUCATION

STATISTICS FOR EDUCATION
AND PHYSICAL EDUCATION

LOUIS COHEN & MICHAEL HOLLIDAY

LOUGHBOROUGH UNIVERSITY OF TECHNOLOGY

Harper & Row, Publishers

London   New York   Hagerstown   Sydney

British Library Cataloguing in Publication Data
Cohen, Louis
  Statistics for education and physical education.
1. Educational statistics
2. Physical education and training—Statistical methods
I. Title II. Holliday, Michael
519.5'02'437   LB2846

ISBN 0 06 318093 6 paperback
     0 06 318092 8 cased

Set by Santype International Ltd
Printed and bound by
The Garden City Press, Letchworth

Harper & Row Ltd
28 Tavistock Street
London WC2E 7PN

*"A child of five would understand this.
Send somebody for a child of five."*
Groucho Marx.

Acknowledgements

Our thanks are due to David Johnson, of the Department of Management Studies, Loughborough University, who read the script and made a number of valuable suggestions; to Margaret Stefanuti of the Postgraduate School of Research in Education, University of Bradford, who painstakingly checked all the calculations, and to Yasmin Dharamshi and Angela Fairmann of the Department of Education, Loughborough University, who managed to transform our handwriting into intelligible typescript.

To all four, our sincere thanks. Whatever faults now remain are our responsibility and ours alone.

Contents

Contents

Omitted [

List of Tables

Statistics for Education and Physical Education

List of Figures

Preface

Few students look forward with relish to a course in statistics. The word itself evokes feelings of apprehension and the thought of working with mathematical formulae causes many to anticipate difficulties that need never arise.

Why the concern?

Many fear that statistics will be too difficult for them to grasp because their knowledge of mathematics is rudimentary and much of what they once knew is now forgotten. We can reassure readers that the level of arithmetical skills and the knowledge of elementary algebra necessary to follow this text are well within the ability of an average 13–14 year old pupil. That said, statistics is a branch of mathematics and the statistical methods and formulae that we introduce are mathematically derived. However, it is neither our intention to present mathematical explanations of statistical techniques, nor at the other extreme, to provide a cookbook of statistical recipes.

One purpose of this text is to help students understand statistical methods so that they can tackle their research problems successfully.

By working through the book carefully and systematically, students should gain a thorough grasp of the most widely used statistics in Education and Physical Education. The text teaches basic statistical methods and their application to those who may lack a strong background in mathematics. In doing so, mathematical derivations of formulae are completely omitted and, apart from a minimal

1

number of essential 'shorthand' mathematical symbols, familiar examples drawn from Education and Physical Education data are presented in a non-mathematical form throughout.

In planning the scope and content of the text, we have in mind the needs of those students who are required to undertake small scale empirical research as part fulfilment of the requirements of the award of Advanced Diplomas and both undergraduate and postgraduate qualifications in Education and Physical Education. Their research needs are often quite specific; first to find an appropriate . design for their particular research topic and second, to apply appropriate statistical tests in the analysis of their data. The first sections of the text teach basic statistics and prepare students to tackle research problems with confidence and intelligence. The latter half of the book ('Choosing an Appropriate Test') provides students with concrete examples drawn from Education and Physical Education data which illustrate the most commonly-used research designs in undergraduate and postgraduate studies. A standard format is employed throughout. It consists of:

1 a tabular presentation of research design

2 a concrete example of the research design using education or physical education data

3 that example is then worked through, using an appropriate statistical test and illustrating each stage of the computation in full.

Introduction

1.1 What Do We Mean By Statistics?

From earliest times man has collected and made use of statistics. He used them six thousand years ago in Upper Egypt, assessing the size of the harvest in order to fix the price of corn until the next flooding of the Nile valley. He used them in Judea and Samaria two thousand years ago, taking head counts of the Jewish tribes in order to exact taxation for Rome. And he used them daily three hundred or so years ago for the grim purpose of assessing the number of dead as the dreaded Plague spread across London and the Home Counties. Statistics has had a venerable and varied history!

Today, statistics is a familiar and accepted aspect of our modern world. We have statistics in the shape of sports results, long range weather forecasts, stockmarket trends, consumer reports, cost of living indices and life insurance premiums. It is impossible to imagine life without some form of statistical information being readily at hand.

The word *statistics* is used in two senses. It refers to collections of quantitative information and methods of handling that sort of data. Domesday Book, that mammoth stocktaking exercise of William the Conqueror, is an example of this first sense in which the word is used. Statistics also refers to the drawing of inferences about large groups on the basis of observations made on smaller ones. The calculation of swings in the nation's party political preferences before an election is based upon information gathered in carefully selected interviews and illustrates the second sense in which the word statistics is used.

Statistics then, is to do with ways of organizing, summarizing and describing quantifiable data, and methods of drawing inferences and generalizing upon them.

1.2 Why is Statistics Necessary?

Apart from the intrusion of statistics upon so many aspects of our daily lives, there are two reasons why some knowledge of statistics is an important part of the professional competence of every teacher. First, statistical literacy is necessary if the teacher is to read and evaluate educational research critically and intelligently. Take, for example, an Infants' teacher asked to choose between two tests of reading readiness. What will she make of information such as, 'split half reliability of the XYZ test is 0.82 ($p < 0.05$)'? And how will a physical education teacher respond to a research report of a coaching experiment in which, 'ANOVA gave an F value of 9.93 with 2 and 33 degrees of freedom ($p < 0.001$)'? Will they both be forced to ignore such information because they lack the statistical understanding to appreciate its meaning and value?

A second reason why statistical literacy is important to teachers is that if they are going to undertake research on their own account, then a grasp of statistical methods is essential. With such understanding our hypothetical Infants' teacher could use the reading readiness test that she selects, describe her results and make inferences from them. Similarly, our physical education teacher could replicate the experiment he has read about and decide for himself whether the special coaching involved in Method A results in a higher level of skill performance on the part of its recipients.

Whether teachers are actively involved in research or not, membership of the teaching profession carries with it an obligation to keep abreast of developments in their specific areas of interest and expertise. Studying research reports, evaluating new techniques and approaches in teaching generally requires acquaintance with statistical principles and methods.

1.3 The Purpose of the Text

The objectives of *Statistics for Education and Physical Education* follow directly from our discussion in 1.2 above. First, the text aims to give students sufficient grounding in statistical principles and methods to enable them to read and understand empirical research findings in those aspects of the social, behavioural, and physical sciences that underpin Education and Physical Education.

Second, the text aims to present research students with a variety of statistical techniques relevant to their research designs and to help them select statistical tests appropriate to the solution of their research problems.

1.4   Limitations of Statistics

Statistical techniques can assist the researcher describe data, design experiments, and test hunches about relationships among the things or events in which he is interested. At best, however, they can only partly inform his professional judgements and decisions. Statistics helps the researcher accept or reject the hunches he has about his data within recognized degrees of confidence – no more, no less. Statistics is simply a tool that can be used to answer problems that are amenable to quantification. Take, for example, the physical education teacher referred to above. Suppose that the results of his experiment show him to be correct in his suspicion that coaching Method A brings about substantial increments in skills performance. This is only one aspect of the necessary range of information he must evaluate in deciding whether or not to introduce the method. What extra costs are involved in terms of teachers' time, expenditure on equipment, re-timetabling the use of gymnasia, etc.? Statistical findings can be an invaluable asset to the teacher, but they are there to guide his educational decisions, not to determine them.

Finally, it hardly needs mentioning that there are innumerable situations in school classrooms and gymnasia, on sports fields and in out-of-school activities that do not lend themselves to quantification or statistical analysis.

Measurement Concepts

2.1 Sources of Data

It appears from the text title that we have identified Education and Physical Education as two completely separate fields of study, but this is not so. They are closely interwoven and at times inseparable. Both are concerned with man's physical, intellectual, social, and emotional development and the environmental factors which influence this development.

It therefore comes as no surprise that the sources of data relevant to these areas are diverse and varied, incorporating the natural and behavioural sciences as well as the humanities. Some sources will be concerned with man's intelligence, his numeracy and literacy skills, his physical skills, his health, his personality, his values, attitudes and beliefs, his family background and social circumstances, his emotional and organic maturity, his aspirations and his achievements.

Often this array of human attributes and accomplishments is somewhat arbitrarily 'parcelled-up' as the particular provinces of various social and physical science disciplines. Psychology, for example, deals with intelligence, learning and personality; social psychology, with values attitudes and beliefs; sociology, with the family and socio-economic circumstances; physiology, with organic function; biomechanics, with the principles and laws governing human performance.

Students in Education and Physical Education, as part of a taught course or personal research, will therefore be gathering, analyzing and interpreting data from many of these and other sources and throughout this text we illustrate statistical techniques with data from these sources to make our examples both interesting and relevant to the reader.

2.2 Populations, Parameters, Samples, and Statistics

We are often required to assemble and evaluate information regarding some common characteristic(s) of a *population*. It must be stressed at this stage that in the widest sense a population is more than just a collection of people. It could refer to a large collection of objects or events which vary in respect of some characteristic(s). All the boys of Hilltown Comprehensive School for example, who serve as subjects for a student's research into the ratio of height to weight, are a population. All the stop watches used in the Olympic games are a population. A population need not be very large, although the procedures set out in this text generally assume the existence of extremely large or infinite populations.

Characteristics of a population which differ from person to person or object to object are called *variables*. Height, weight, age, intelligence, anxiety differences, reading ability, fitness, to name but a few, are examples of human variables and to these variables we can assign numbers or values.

Once numbers or values are assigned to the population characteristics we can measure them. The measures which describe population characteristics are called *parameters*.

It is not always practical to obtain measures from a total population due to factors such as expense, time, accessibility, etc., and so the researcher has to collect his information from a smaller group or 'sub set' of the population, assuming that the information gained is representative of the whole population under study. This smaller group or 'sub set' is known as a *sample*. Suppose the population of Hilltown school is 800. This is a large number of subjects for even the most ambitious student researcher to handle. He would probably settle for some part of that population, choosing a representative sample of say 80 subjects on the basis of their ages or numbers in each class. (The various methods of selecting representative samples from their populations are discussed in Sections 9.2 to 9.7.)

The measures taken from a sample describing the sample characteristics are called *statistics* and it is from these statistics that the population parameters are estimated. The height to weight ratios of the Hilltown sample are used to predict the Hilltown population height to weight ratio parameter.

The relationship between populations, parameters, samples, and statistics is represented in Figure 1. A simple way of remembering this relationship is that statistic is to sample as parameter is to population.

Figure 1 Populations, parameters, samples, and statistics.

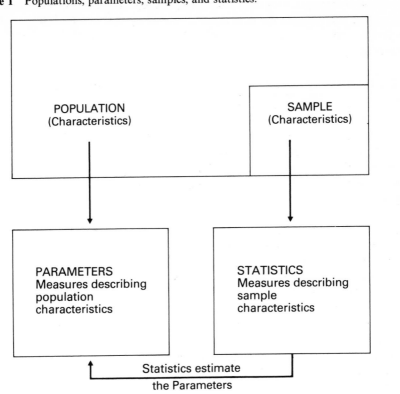

2.3 Descriptive and Inferential Statistics

Descriptive statistics are used to organize, summarize, and describe measures of a sample. No predictions or inferences are made regarding the population parameters. For example, from our sample of Hilltown schoolchildren we could work out the average height to weight ratio, or the most common height to weight ratio, to name but two descriptive measures. At this descriptive level no attempt would be made to predict population parameters.

Inferential or inductive statistics, on the other hand, are used to infer or predict population parameters from sample measures. This is done by a process of inductive reasoning based on the mathematical theory of probability. From our Hilltown sample it would be possible, using appropriate mathematical techniques, to estimate or predict from the average score what the population average score would probably be. However, no one can predict exactly the population measures from sample measures, only a 'probable' measure. How closely this probable measure would be to the exact measure would depend upon the sample selection procedures and the statistical techniques used.

2.4 Parametric and Non Parametric Statistics

It stands to reason that in order to predict from sample data, the population measures have to a lesser or greater extent to be predictable. The mathematician must know or assume certain factors regarding the population measures in order to have a base from which to derive his statistical method. Statistical methods of inference which depend upon knowing or assuming certain population factors are called *parametric* methods and are the oldest and most often used.

In practice however it is not always possible to be able to predict or make assumptions about the population measures. More recently methods have been evolved which are not based upon the stringent assumptions of population measures. These methods are called *non parametric* methods.

It would be inappropriate at this point in the text when foundations are being laid, to enlarge on the complexities of the two basic methods until we have discussed in detail the properties of population and sample measures. The advantages and disadvantages of parametric and non parametric techniques in Education and Physical Education are discussed in detail in Section 9.18.

Classifying Data

3.1 Scales of Measurement

Almost every page of *Statistics for Education and Physical Education* is concerned with classifying, categorizing and quantifying individuals, objects, and events in order to examine relationships between them. Whether the objective is to record the verbal behaviour of a teacher, the running times of a junior athlete, or the readability level of an Infant primer, underlying the specific classification scheme is the fact that the variables themselves are *measurable*. Variables that are measurable are capable of being placed at some point along a continuum against which numerals may be assigned according to certain rules. Measurement transforms organized and classified data into familiar amenable things called *numbers*.

Generally, four levels of measurement or four ways of assigning numerals can be distinguished. They are referred to as *nominal, ordinal, interval,* and *ratio* scales. Each level has its own rules and restrictions, each level moreover is hierarchical in that each higher level or scale incorporates the properties of the lower.

3.2 The Nominal Scale

The most elementary scale in measurement is one which does no more than identify the categories into which individuals, objects, or events may be classified.

Those categories have to be mutually exclusive of course. That is to say, one cannot place an individual into more than one category. When numbers are assigned to such categories, as they often are in research, they have no numerical meaning; rather they are simply convenient ways of labelling or coding the information. For example, in coding up a fieldwork project, the researcher may assign the label '1' to adult males, '2' to adult females, '3' to male children, and '4' to female children. Such labels have no quantitative meaning. They cannot be added, subtracted, multiplied or divided; their function is purely to identify categories that are different. Notice one other feature of a nominal scale illustrated in our '1', '2', '3', '4', example. A nominal scale should also be *complete*, that is, it should include all possible classifications of a particular type.

3.3 The Ordinal Scale

The ordinal scale of measurement incorporates the classifying and labelling function of the nominal scale, but in addition it brings to it a sense of order. Ordinal numbers are used to indicate rank order and nothing more. The ordinal scale is used to arrange individuals or objects in a series ranging from the highest to the lowest according to the particular characteristic being measured. The ordinal numbers assigned to such a series do not indicate absolute quantities, nor can it be assumed that the intervals between the numbers are equal. For example, in a group of children rated by an observer on the degree of their co-operativeness and ranged from highest to lowest according to that attribute, it cannot be assumed that the difference in the degree of co-operativeness between subjects one and two is the same as that obtaining between subjects nine and ten; nor can it be taken that subject one possesses ten times the quantity of co-operativeness of subject ten.

3.4 The Interval Scale

As the term 'interval' implies, in addition to rank-ordering the data, the interval scale allows us to state *precisely how far apart* are the individuals, the objects or the events that form the focus of our inquiry. Interval scales (or as they are sometimes called *equal-interval* scales) permit certain mathematical procedures previously untenable at nominal and ordinal levels of measurements. Because we can legitimately say that the difference between the scores of, say, the eighth and ninth pupils is equal to the difference between the scores of the second and third, it follows that the intervals can be added or subtracted.

In our example of pupils' scores above we cannot, of course, assume that the score of the third child is three times the score of the ninth individual, for one limitation of the interval scale is that there is no absolute zero point. A zero score on an intelligence test, for example, does not mean that the particular testee has no intelligence whatsoever. In most school tests however, it is not necessary to define absolute zero knowledge or absolute zero achievement, since very often the objective of the testing procedure is to compare children one with another or to compare their performance with a conventionally-accepted criterion level such as $40\% = $ pass and $70\% = $ distinction.

3.5 The Ratio Scale

The highest level of measurement, and the one which subsumes interval, ordinal, and nominal levels, is the ratio scale. A ratio scale includes an absolute zero, it provides equal intervals, it gives a rank ordering, and it can be used for simple labelling purposes. Because there is an absolute zero, all of the arithmetical processes of addition, subtraction, multiplication and division are possible. Whereas few, if any, educational and psychological tests can assume ratio level measurement, it is in the physical sciences that zero ratio scales are meaningfully utilized. Using weight as an illustration of a ratio scale we can say that no mass at all is a zero measure and that 1000 grams is 400 grams heavier than 600 grams and twice as heavy as 500.

3.6 Discrete and Continuous Variables

The task of the student researcher is to collect, organize, and analyze data from variables. As mentioned earlier these variables are capable of being assigned numbers or values. The nature of these numbers or values will depend upon whether the variables are classified as *discrete* or *continuous*.

A discrete variable is a variable which can take on numerals or values that are specific distinct points on a scale. For example *sex* is a discrete variable. A person is either male or female and cannot be assigned any value between the two. The number of players in a football team is a discrete variable. It is possible to have only 1, 2, 3, 4, 5, 6, 7, 8, 9, 10, or 11 players, but not $7\frac{1}{2}$.

A continuous variable is a variable that, theoretically at least, can take on any value between two points on a scale. It can be measured with differing degrees of exactness depending on the measuring instrument. For example, weight is a continuous variable. It can take on any number of possible values between 0 and infinity. Height, time, distance jumped, percentage body fat, haemoglobin level are a few other examples related to physical education.

It must be made clear however, that this distinction between discrete and continuous variables is often only a theoretical one and in practice, because of the lack of suitable measuring instruments, many continuous variables have to be assigned whole number values. Intelligence Quotient theoretically is a continuous variable, but in practice the tests used to measure it give whole numbers or discrete scores.

3.7 Limits of Numbers

Because of certain problems in measuring on continuous scales, most variables are given discrete values. In order to interpret such values, account is taken of the mathematical *true limits* of a number. In general, true limits of a number are said to extend one half a unit below and one half a unit above that number and any score within those limits is rounded off to the number.

For example, if after a performance test it was found that ten students scored 90, does this really mean that they are all equal in performance ability? The likelihood of them all being exactly alike in ability is extremely small. It is more likely that some scored just below 90 and some scored just above 90, but the measuring instrument was not sophisticated enough to detect the differences.

To overcome this problem the number 90 is said to have limits ranging from 89.5 to 90.5 and any scores between those limits are given to score 90.

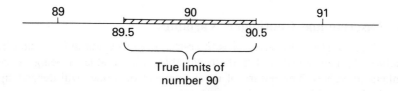

Further examples

1. Limits of score 7

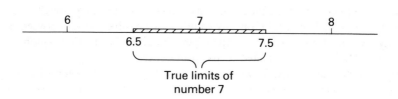

2. Limits of score 20.5

Limits of score 20.5

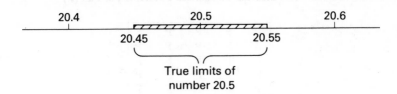

Note that it is not just *whole* numbers that have limits. Any number has limits.

This 'true limit' concept is particularly useful when classifying scores into groups or intervals. For example, if we wanted to find out from the test just mentioned how many people scored between 80 and 90 (Interval A) and 90 and 100 (Interval B), in which interval do we include those people who scored 90? The problem is usually solved by considering the true limits of the intervals. Interval A really extends from 79.5 to 89.5 and Interval B from 89.5 to 99.5.

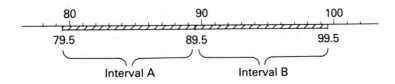

Therefore all those scoring 90 would be included in Interval B.

3.8 The Frequency Table

The problem that confronts the researcher once he has collected his results is what to do with them.

His first priority must be to organize and summarize the data in a form that allows further interpretation and analysis. This is done by constructing a frequency table or frequency distribution which arranges scores into groups or classes.

Suppose 25 students were observed at interview for entry into a college and given a rating of Pass or Fail. The raw data could be presented as in Table 1.

Table 1 Observations of 25 Students Categorized as Pass (P) or Fail (F)

P	F	P	P	F
F	F	P	F	P
P	F	F	F	F
F	P	F	F	P
P	F	P	F	F

These observations as yet have little meaning. They have not been organized or summarized. This is done by constructing a frequency table as in Table 2.

Table 2 Frequency Distribution of 25 Students Classified as Pass or Fail

Column 1	Column 2	Column 3
Rating	Frequency (f)	Percentage (p)
Pass	10	40
Fail	15	60
Total 25		100%

Table 2 shows how the two categories, pass and fail, have been separated (column 1). The number of people who passed or failed have been entered in column 2, next to the appropriate category. The number of observations in a particular category are called frequencies (f). The pass/fail frequencies have been converted to percentages in column 3.

The information in Table 2 can be graphically presented as shown in Section 4.2.

In the example above the data are discrete. Since much of the data in Education and Physical Education are collected from continuous rather than discrete variables, raw scores have to be dealt with. Raw scores can also be organized and summarized by means of a frequency table.

Suppose the following scores were obtained after testing 50 college students on standing vertical high jump ability (Sargent Jump).

Table 3 **Standing Vertical High Jump Scores of 50 College Students (measured in cms.)**

52	78	63	58	64	73	57	76	67	77
60	64	54	64	49	67	62	53	70	86
61	46	74	69	80	71	56	71	72	66
59	62	64	52	65	82	68	67	90	81
78	58	55	69	83	65	50	70	77	66

The data in Table 3 can be summarized and grouped as shown in the frequency Table 4 below.

3.9 Steps in the Construction of Table 4

1 Determine the range of scores. The highest score minus the lowest score plus 1. (One is added to take into account the true limits of the numbers.)

Range = Highest score (90) − Lowest score (46) + 1
$$= (90 - 46) + 1$$
$$= 45$$

2 Decide on how many categories or step intervals are required. Normally the number of intervals used is not less than 10 and not more than 20.

In this case we have selected 15 as a convenient number of step intervals.

3 Divide the range by the number of step intervals giving the actual size of each step interval.

Step Interval size = $\frac{45}{15} = 3$

If the step interval size does not work out to be a whole number it is advisable to round it off, easing the arithmetical load. For example, if we had chosen 12 step intervals, the step interval size would have worked out to be $\frac{45}{12} = 3.7$ and this would round off to 4.

Table 4   Frequency Distribution of Standing Vertical High Jump Scores of 50 College Students (measured in cms.)

Step Intervals (True Limits)	Step Intervals (Limits rounded off)	Tallies	Frequency (f)
87.5–90.5	88–91	I	1
84.5–87.5	85–88	I	1
81.5–84.5	82–85	II	2
78.5–81.5	79–82	II	2
75.5–78.5	76–79	IIIII	5
72.5–75.5	73–76	II	2
69.5–72.5	70–73	IIIII	5
66.5–69.5	67–70	IIIIII	6
63.5–66.5	64–67	IIIIIIII	8
60.5–63.5	61–64	IIII	4
57.5–60.5	58–61	IIII	4
54.5–57.5	55–58	III	3
51.5–54.5	52–55	IIII	4
48.5–51.5	49–52	II	2
45.5–48.5	46–49	I	1
			$N = 50$

4   Construct the step interval column starting with the lower limit of the lowest score (45.5). Add the step interval size (3) to this lower limit. The range of the lowest step interval becomes 45.5–48.5. The lower limit of the next interval becomes 48.5 to which 3 is added to give interval range 48.5–51.5. This procedure is repeated, moving up the table until the step interval column includes an interval into which the highest score (90) can be placed, namely, 87.5–90.5.

As can be seen from the table, we have included two step interval columns. One uses the exact limits of the step intervals and the other rounded off limits. It is recommended that the inexperienced student statistician uses true limits of step intervals to avoid confusion.

5 Insert, in the column provided, a tally for each individual score in the raw data table. For example, for the score 52, a tally or mark is inserted to show it falls into the step interval 51.5–54.5.

6 Total up the tallies within each step interval and place in the frequency column in line with the appropriate interval.

7 Total the frequency column (N). This serves as a useful check that all the data have been included in the table.

Presenting Data

4.1 Introduction

One drawback in presenting data in the form of a frequency table is that the information contained there does not become immediately apparent unless the table is studied in detail. To simplify the interpretation of the information, the data are often processed further and transformed into a visual presentation which can be more readily comprehended.

The most common methods of presenting data are based upon graphical techniques. In this section we describe five methods suitable for presenting Education and Physical Education data.

4.2 Bar Graph

Portraying information by means of a bar graph is particularly useful when dealing with data gathered from discrete variables that are measured on a nominal scale such as the pass/fail results shown in Table 2.

A bar graph uses rectangles (i.e. bars) to represent discrete categories of data, the length of the bar being proportional to the number of frequencies within that category. Using data from Table 2, the following bar graph can be constructed.

Figure 2 Bar graph showing the frequency distribution of pass/fail categories.

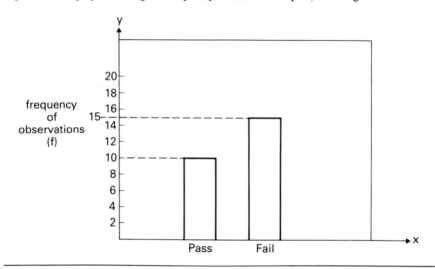

The categories are placed on the horizontal base line (the *x* axis or abscissa) with each category, pass or fail, being assigned a bar. The width of the bar is arbitrary but it is recommended that all bars should be the same in width. The vertical line (the *y* axis or ordinate) is marked off to scale, indicating the observed frequencies in each category.

4.3   Histogram

The histogram is similar to the bar graph, the only difference in presentation being that the bars are joined together.

Joining the bars together makes the histogram a suitable method for presenting data gathered from continuous variables measured on interval or ratio scales.

The vertical jump data set out in Table 4 can be represented by the histogram in Figure 3.

Each bar represents a step interval as defined in Table 4, the exact limits of the intervals producing a continuous scale along the base line of the graph. The width of each bar is the size of each step interval (3) and the height of each bar is proportional to the frequencies within that interval. The histogram gives an immediate picture of how the scores are distributed.

Figure 3 Histogram showing the frequency distribution of 50 vertical jump scores (raw data from Table 4).

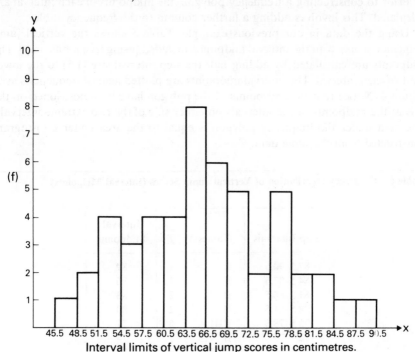

Interval limits of vertical jump scores in centimetres.

4.4 Frequency Polygon

Another commonly used graphical technique is the frequency polygon. This form of presentation dispenses with the use of bars and employs single points joined together by a series of straight lines. The reader will recognize the similarity of this approach to basic graphing techniques in mathematics.

The single point in the frequency polygon is placed at the midpoint of the step interval at a height proportional to the frequencies within an interval.

Prior to constructing a frequency polygon, the midpoints of each interval are calculated. This involves adding a further column to the frequency table.

Using the data in our previous example, Table 5 shows the vertical jump frequency scores with the interval midpoints included (using true limits only). The midpoints are calculated by adding half the step interval size (1.5) to the lower limit of each interval. The interval midpoints are plotted against frequencies as in Figure 4. Notice that the end points of the polygon have been positioned on the axis at the midpoints of the intervals on either side of the two extreme intervals. The area under the frequency polygon is equal to the area under a histogram constructed from the same data.

Table 5   Frequency Distribution of Vertical Jump Scores (Interval Midpoints)

Step Intervals	Tallies	f	Interval Midpoints
87.5–90.5	I	1	89
84.5–87.5	I	1	86
81.5–84.5	II	2	83
78.5–81.5	II	2	80
75.5–78.5	IIIII	5	77
72.5–75.5	II	2	74
69.5–72.5	IIIII	5	71
66.5–69.5	IIIIII	6	68
63.5–66.5	IIIIIIII	8	65
60.5–63.5	IIII	4	62
57.5–60.5	IIII	4	59
54.5–57.5	III	3	56
51.5–54.5	IIII	4	53
48.5–51.5	II	2	50
45.5–48.5	I	1	47

Figure 4   Frequency polygon for vertical jump scores in Table 5.

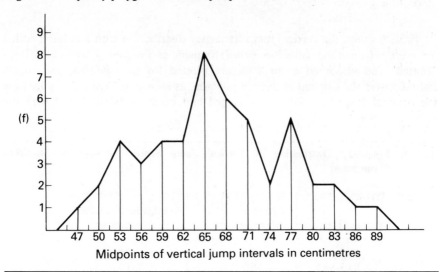

Midpoints of vertical jump intervals in centimetres

4.5   Smoothed Frequency Polygon

Occasionally the researcher wishes to know what sort of frequency distribution he would have obtained had the data been collected from a larger sample or a whole population. He can get some indication of this by smoothing the original polygon. In theory, the larger the number of results that one processes, the nearer the distribution approximates a curve. Care must be taken however, as smoothing can only give an impression of what the distribution might have been, *not* what is actually is.

Smoothing a frequency polygon requires the calculation of average frequencies for each interval. The *average frequency* for any interval is calculated by adding the frequency of that interval to the frequencies of the two adjacent intervals, and dividing the total by 3.

For example, using the data in Table 5, the average frequency for the interval 48.5–51.5 is the frequency of that interval (2), added to the frequency of the interval 45.5–48.5 (1) and the frequency of the interval 51.5–54.5, (4), divided by 3.

$$\frac{2 + 1 + 4}{3} = 2.3$$

This is repeated for each of the step intervals. Where an interval has only one adjacent interval, then the missing interval is given a frequency of 0.

25

For example, for the interval 45.5–48.5, the average frequency is,

$$\frac{0 + 1 + 2}{3} = 1$$

Table 6 shows the vertical jump frequency distribution with a column added for average (sometimes called *smoothed*) frequencies. Frequency tallies have been omitted. The smoothed frequencies are plotted for each interval and superimposed over the original frequency polygon, as shown in Figure 5. Notice how the original frequency polygon is jagged and irregular as compared with the smoothed one.

Table 6   Frequency Distribution of Vertical Jump Scores (Average or Smoothed Frequencies)

Step Intervals	Interval Midpoints	f	Average (or Smoothed) Frequencies
87.5–90.5	89	1	0.6
84.5–87.5	86	1	1.3
81.5–84.5	83	2	1.6
78.5–81.5	80	2	3.0
75.5–78.5	77	5	3.0
72.5–75.5	74	2	4.0
69.5–72.5	71	5	4.3
66.5–69.5	68	6	6.3
63.5–66.5	65	8	6.0
60.5–63.5	62	4	5.3
57.5–60.5	59	4	3.6
54.5–57.5	56	3	3.6
51.5–54.5	53	4	3.0
48.5–51.5	50	2	2.3
45.5–48.5	47	1	1.0

Figure 5 Smoothed frequency polygon for vertical jump scores in Table 6.

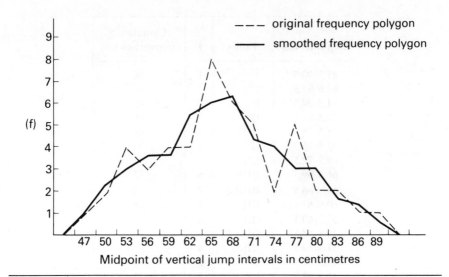

Midpoint of vertical jump intervals in centimetres

4.6   Cumulative Frequency Graph or Ogive

A fourth method of presenting data in a graphical form is the cumulative frequency graph or ogive. This method is particularly useful when the researcher wishes to know how many scores lie below either an individual or a step interval score. The utility of this technique will become clear later in the text when we discuss measures of relative position.

We begin to construct the ogive by adding the scores in our frequency table *serially*. Scores that are added serially are accumulated progressively starting with the bottom interval of the distribution. The cumulative frequency for any given interval is the frequency of that interval added to the total frequencies below that interval. For example, using our vertical jump data once again, the cumulative frequency for interval 54.5–57.5 is

3 + 4 + 2 + 1 = 10

Table 7 shows the original frequency distribution with a cumulative frequency column included. The cumulative frequency graph is plotted with the scores or step interval along the horizontal axis and the *cumulative frequencies* along the vertical axis (see Figure 6 below).

Table 7   Cumulative Frequency Distribution of Vertical Jump Scores

Step Intervals	Tallies	f	Cumulative frequencies (cf)
87.5–90.5	I	1	50
84.5–87.5	I	1	49
81.5–84.5	II	2	48
78.5–81.5	II	2	46
75.5–78.5	IIIII	5	44
72.5–75.5	II	2	39
69.5–72.5	IIIII	5	37
66.5–69.5	IIIIII	6	32
63.5–66.5	IIIIIIII	8	26
60.5–63.5	IIII	4	18
57.5–60.5	IIII	4	14
54.5–57.5	III	3	10
51.5–54.5	IIII	4	7
48.5–51.5	II	2	3
45.5–48.5	I	1	1

Figure 6   Cumulative frequency graph for vertical jump data in Table 7.

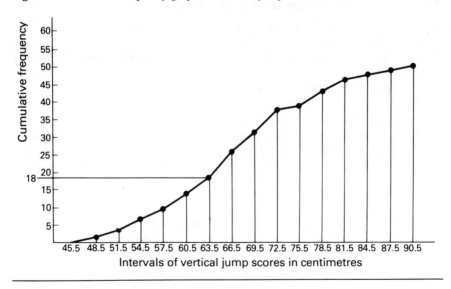

The difference between this graph and the normal frequency polygon is that it is not the actual frequencies that are plotted, but cumulative frequencies. Moreover, the cumulative frequencies must be plotted at the upper limit of each step interval as they include the frequencies in that interval. For example, the cumulative frequency for the interval 60.5–63.5, (18), is plotted at point 63.5 on the vertical axis.

Cumulative frequency graphs can be smoothed in the same way that frequency polygons can be smoothed.

4.7 The Circle or Pie Graph

The last of the five methods of presenting data is best suited to simple comparisons of data to do with discrete variables. It is based on proportioning a circle to equivalent percentage proportions of the frequency distribution.

For example, from our data on pass/fail students, we determined the percentage of passes and fails as 40% and 60% respectively. A circle is drawn, the area of which represents 100% of the observations. Two lines are then drawn dividing the total area. We can work out the precise positioning of the dividing lines using 360° to represent 100%. 40% is then represented by an angle of 144°, that is

$$\frac{40}{100} \times 360 = 144$$

The choice of method used in presenting data in a graphical form must rest upon the nature of the initial data and the amount of detailed visual information that is required. Remember, pictorial methods of presentation add nothing to the data that isn't already there to begin with! Their task is simply to display it more effectively.

Figure 7 Circle or pie graph of pass/fail ratings.

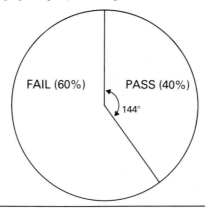

Measuring Typical Achievement

5.1 Introduction

We said in 1.1 above that one meaning of statistics is to do with describing quantitative data. Suppose those data are scores on an arithmetic test. Describing such a set of scores involves giving information about two aspects of their composition.

Arithmetic scores like many other tests of achievement tend to cluster together about the centre. One description of our data, then, is to do with the *central tendency* of the scores. The three descriptive statistics that we will consider, the mean, the median and the mode, provide information about how a distribution of scores is centred or grouped together.

A second aspect of the composition of our arithmetical data is to do with the *variability* of the scores, that is, the way in which they are spread out from the centre of the distribution. We deal with variability in Sections 6.2 to 6.9.

5.2 Calculating the Mean from Ungrouped Data

The mean (M) is the most familiar and useful measure used to describe the central tendency or average of a distribution of scores for any group of individuals, objects or events. The mean is computed by dividing the sum of the scores by the total number of scores.

The formula is given as:

$$M = \frac{\sum X}{N}$$

where X is each score

              N is the total number of scores

and $\sum$ means 'the sum of'

Example   The scores of 8 pupils on a spelling quiz are recorded below:

$$
\begin{array}{r}
16 \\
11 \\
13 \\
20 \\
15 \\
18 \\
10 \\
\underline{17} \\
\sum X = 120
\end{array}
$$

$$M = \frac{\sum X}{N} = \frac{120}{8} = 15$$

5.3 Calculating the Mean from Grouped Data

In the example above we used the *ungrouped* scores of 8 pupils as our data. Suppose, however, that we are to compute the mean when we have scores that have already been *grouped*. The calculation of the mean from grouped data is slightly different.

Example   The scores of 20 pupils on a road-safety test have been arranged in *groups of five*, ranging from a group scoring 5–9 who have little knowledge of road safety, to a very knowledgeable group, scoring 30–34.

The formula for computing the mean from grouped data is given as:

$$M = \frac{\sum fX}{N}$$

where X is the midpoint of a class interval
           f is the number of cases in that interval
           N is the total number of scores

and $\sum$ means 'the sum of'

Table 8   Computing the Mean from Grouped Data

Road safety grouped scores (exact limits)	X Midpoint of the interval	f	fX
29.5–34.5	32	2	64
24.5–29.5	27	2	54
19.5–24.5	22	5	110
14.5–19.5	17	6	102
9.5–14.5	12	4	48
4.5– 9.5	7	1	7
		$N = 20$	$385 = \sum fX$

$$M = \frac{\sum fX}{N} = \frac{385}{20} = 19.25$$

5.4 A Short Method of Calculating the Mean from Grouped Data

There is a shorter way of calculating the mean from grouped data which saves time and labour in computation, particularly when one has to deal with a large number of cases. It involves making a guess at identifying the interval in which the mean probably falls. Look at the frequency distribution (column f) in Table 8 above. The mean is probably contained either in interval 19.5–24.5 or in interval 14.5–19.5. Let's assume that it occurs in interval 14.5–19.5. Our *guessed* or *assumed* mean (A.M.) then becomes the midpoint of that interval, that is to say, A.M. = 17.

Table 9 Computing the Mean from Grouped Data (Short Method)

Road safety grouped scores (exact limits)	X Midpoint of the interval	f	d	fd	
29.5–34.5	32	2	+3	+6	
24.5–29.5	27	2	+2	+4	
19.5–24.5	22	5	+1	+5	(+15)
14.5–19.5 ← A.M.	17	6	0		
9.5–14.5	12	4	−1	−4	
4.5– 9.5	7	1	−2	−2	(−6)
		$N = 20$		$\sum fd = +9$	

1 In Table 9 in the column headed d, we place the value 0 next to the interval containing our assumed mean (A.M. = 17). The first interval above the one containing the assumed mean is assigned the value +1, the one above is given the value +2, and the third interval above is given the value +3. Below the interval containing the assumed mean, the first interval is assigned the value −1, the second, −2. These values represent the deviations (d) of the midpoints of the various intervals from the assumed mean in units of class intervals.

2 The deviations in column d are multiplied by their respective frequencies (f) to give the products recorded in column fd. These are summed algebraically, the 'positives' first, then the 'negatives'. The total ($\sum fd$) is recorded at the bottom of column fd.

3 By dividing $\sum fd$ by N, the total number of scores in the frequency column (f), we obtain C^i, a correction factor in class interval units:

$$C^i = \frac{\sum fd}{N} = \frac{9}{20} = 0.45$$

4 By multiplying C^i by our interval ($i = 5$) we obtain the correction factor C which can then be applied to our assumed mean (A.M.) in order to transform it into the true mean (M).

$$C = C^i i = .45 \times 5 = 2.25$$

5 The assumed mean plus the correction factor gives the true mean.

A.M. + C = M

17 + 2.25 = 19.25

5.5   The Median

Another useful measure of central tendency is the *median* or *middle score.*

The median is simply that point on a scale of measurement above which there are exactly half the scores and below which there are the other half of the scores.

In the distribution 1, 3, 5, 7, 9, 11, 13, the middle score is 7. Thus the score of seven indicates the median point at which there are three scores above and three scores below. We obtain the median by arranging the scores in ascending order from the smallest to the greatest score and selecting that point above and below which there are an equal number of scores.

The median point in a distribution of scores, the total of which comes to an odd number is the middle score in that distribution providing that the middle score has a frequency of one.

2,   3,   5,   7,   9,   10,   12,   13,   14,   16,   18,   20,   21

↑

median point

Where the middle score in a distribution has a frequency greater than one, it is necessary to understand the meaning of the *interval of a score* in order to calculate the median point.

The *interval of a score* defines the *exact limits* of that score. The interval ranges from 0.50 units below to 0.50 units above the score. Thus the score six includes all values within the limits of 5.50 to 6.50. The exact midpoint of the interval having lower and upper limits ranging from 5.50 to 6.50 is 6.

In the distribution below, the score of 5 has a frequency of three:

2,   3,   3,   4,   ,5, ⌈ 5,   5, , 7,   9,   10

The exact limits, that is, the interval range of 5, includes all values from 4.50 to 5.50. We assume that the scores 5, 5, 5 are equally spread throughout the interval of 4.50 to 5.50. Thus, each 5 occupies $\frac{1}{3}$ (0.33) of that interval as illustrated below:

| 5 | 5 | 5 |

4.50 4.83 5.16 5.50

The median point of the distribution 2, 3, 3, 4, 5, 5, 5, 7, 9, 10 is to be found between the fifth and the sixth scores. Below the interval 4.50 to 5.50 there are four scores (2, 3, 3, 4). The fifth score (5) is thus $\frac{1}{3}$ of the distance into the interval 4.50 to 5.50, that is 4.50 + 0.33 = 4.83. The median is shown in the diagram below:

⟨.5.....5.....5.⟩

$$: \underline{\quad} : \underline{\quad} : \underline{\quad} : \underline{\quad} : \underline{\quad} : \underline{\quad} : \underline{\quad} : \underline{\quad} : \underline{\quad} : \underline{\quad} :$$
2   3   3   4   4.50 4.83 5.16 5.50 7   9   10

↑

Median

Look at the distribution below:

3, 4, 4, 5, 5, 5, 5, 6, 7

↑

There is an odd number of scores in the distribution, the median being located at the point indicated by the arrow, that is, within the group of four 5s. Again, we assume that the scores 5, 5, 5, 5 are equally spread throughout the interval 4.50 to 5.50. Thus each 5 occupies $\frac{1}{4}$ (0.25) of the interval as illustrated below:

| 5 | 5 | 5 | 5 |

4.50 4.75 5.00 5.25 5.50

The median point of the distribution 3, 4, 4, 5, 5, 5, 5, 6, 7 is to be found midway between 4.75 and 5.00, that is, at a point $4.75 + \frac{1}{2}$ of $(0.25) = 4.875$ (4.88).

⟨.5.....5.....5.....5.⟩

$$: \underline{\quad} : \underline{\quad} : \underline{\quad} : \underline{\quad} : \underline{\quad} : \underline{\quad} : \underline{\quad} : \underline{\quad} : \underline{\quad} :$$
3   4   4   4.50 4.75 5.00 5.25 5.50 6   7

↑

Median
4.88

Look at the distribution below:

53, 54, 55, 59, 62, 67, 70, 71

The median is located between the fourth and the fifth scores, that is, at a point between the upper exact limit of 59 (59.50) and the lower exact limit of 62 (61.50). The diagram below shows that the median is located at 60.50.

$$: \underline{\quad} : \underline{\quad} : \underline{\quad} : \underline{\quad} : \underline{\quad} : \underline{\quad} :$$
59 59.50 60 60.50 61 61.50 62

↑

Median
60.50

5.6   Calculating the Median

Finding the median score in the frequency distribution below involves five steps.

Example   Frequency distribution of 'sit-up' scores in a class of 14-year-old boys.

Class interval	Frequency
48–50	2
45–47	3
42–44	4
39–41	6
36–38	8
33–35	8
30–32	7
27–29	6
24–26	3
21–23	2
18–20	1

$N = 50$

1   Divide the total number of scores by two.

$(50 \div 2 = 25)$

2   Start at the low end of the frequency distribution and sum the scores in each interval until the interval containing the median (i.e. the 25th score) is reached.

$(1 + 2 + 3 + 6 + 7 = 19)$

3   Subtract the sum obtained in step two above from the number necessary to reach the median.

$(25 - 19 = 6)$

4   Now calculate the proportion of the median interval that must be added to its lower limit in order to reach the median score. This is done by dividing the number obtained in step 3 above by the number of scores in the median interval and then multiplying by the size of the class interval.

$\frac{6}{8} \times 3 = \frac{18}{8} = 2.25$

5 Finally, add the number obtained in step 4 above to the exact lower limit of the median interval.

$(32.5 + 2.25 = 34.75)$

Median = 34.75

5.7 Summary

The formula below summarizes the calculation of the median:

$$\text{Median} = L + \left(\frac{\frac{N}{2} - S}{f} \right) \times i$$

where: L = the exact lower limit of the median interval

N = the total number of scores

S = the sum of the scores in the intervals below L

f = the number of scores in the median interval

i = the size of the class interval.

5.8 The Mode

The mode is yet another measure of central tendency. In its most common usage this measure is sometimes referred to as the *crude mode*, that is, the most frequently occurring score in a distribution. The crude mode is rarely applied to ungrouped data. The reason is obvious enough. Any particular score might occur haphazardly at any point in a series of observations and be quite unrepresentative of the data as a whole.

With grouped data one cannot identify the score that occurs most frequently, because that score is lost within a specific interval of the grouped data. One can, however, identify the *modal class*, that is the interval that contains more scores than any other. When the mean and the median have also been determined, the *computed mode* can be obtained from the formula:

Computed mode = 3 × Median − 2 × Mean

5.9 Choosing a Measure of Central Tendency

It's sometimes a problem for the student to decide which of the three measures of central tendency to use, the *mean*, the *median*, or the *mode*, as being most appropriate to his particular research problem. The following advice may be of help.

The mean is doubtless the most commonly-used measure of central tendency. It is the only one of the three measures which uses all of the information available in a set of data, that is to say, it reflects the value of each score in the distribution. It has the decided advantage of being capable of combination with the means of other groups measured on the same variable. For example, from the mean speeds over 100 metres in each of five first year secondary school classes, we can compute an overall first-year mean time for that event. Because neither the median nor the mode is arithmetically-based, this useful application is not possible. The precisely-defined mathematical value of the mean allows other advanced statistical techniques to be based upon it too.

There are occasions, however, when taking into account the value of every score in distribution can give a distorted picture of the data. Imagine the following distribution of press-ups by a small group of boys where one individual's score is extraordinarily different from the rest of the group. (Our data are, of course, hypothetical, but look at the world press-up record of a 13-year-old in the Guinness Book of Records 1976!)

4, 6, 6, 8, 81

Without the very atypical score of 81, the mean score of the group is 6 and the median, likewise, is 6. The effect of introducing the score of 81 is to pull the mean in the direction of that extreme value. The mean now becomes 21, a value that is unrepresentative of the group's performance. The median remains 6, providing a more realistic description of the distribution than the mean.

With these observations in mind:

5.10 Use the Mean

1 When the scores in a distribution are more or less symmetrically grouped about a central point.

2 When the research problem requires a measure of central tendency that will also form the basis of other statistics such as measures of variability (see Section 6.1) or measures of association (see Section 8.1).

3 When the research problem requires the combination of the mean with the means of other groups measured on the same variable.

4 Recalling our discussion of the relationship between a *sample* and a *population* (see Section 2.2), use the mean to measure the central tendency in a sample of observations when one needs to estimate the value of a corresponding mean of the population from which the sample is taken.

5.11   Use the Median

1   When the research problem calls for knowledge of the exact midpoint of a distribution.

2   When extreme scores distort the mean as in our hypothetical press-ups example. The mean reflects extreme values, the median does not.

3   When dealing with 'oddly-shaped' distributions, for example, those in which a high proportion of extremely high scores occur as well as a low proportion of extremely low ones.

5.12   Use the Mode

1   When all that is required is a quick and approximate way of determining central tendency.

2   When in referring to what is 'average', the word is used in the sense of the 'typical' or the 'most usual'. For example, in talking about the average take-home pay of the coalface worker, it is the modal wage that is being alluded to rather than an exact arithmetic average.

Finally, referring to our earlier discussion of scales of measurement in Section 3.1, the *mode* would be the appropriate statistic to use as a measure of the 'most fashionable' or 'most popular' when data are collected using a nominal scale. The *median* would generally be associated with ordinal level data. The *mean* would be used with interval level or ratio level data providing that the distribution of scores approximates a normal curve. It is to a description of the normal curve that we now turn.

5.13   The Normal Curve

At the beginning of most introductory text books concerned with research in Education and Physical Education the reader is confronted with a lovely bell-shaped curve known as the *normal probability curve* (see Figure 8).

Figure 8   The normal curve.

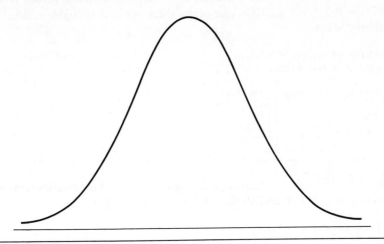

To be strictly correct, one refers to normal probability *curves* rather than the *normal curve*. Three such curves are shown in Figure 9. They differ from each other in their respective 'spreads', a point that we enlarge upon shortly.

Figure 9   Some normal curves.

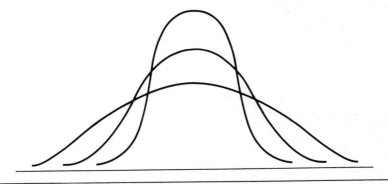

Very often, coin-tossing is the way in which the student is introduced to the idea of probability and to some of the important properties of the normal curve.

Imagine that we have ten pennies all perfectly symmetrical so that none of them is more likely to fall 'heads' than 'tails' when tossed.

When one of those pennies is tossed we know that the chances of tossing 'heads' is one in two; equally, the chances of tossing 'tails' is one in two. With two pennies tossed simultaneously four times, there are four probable results. These are shown below:

Distribution of chances of falls when
two coins are tossed 4 times

Chances in 4 Throws	Two Heads (2H)	One Heads and One Tails (1H)(1T)	Two Tails (2T)
	1	2	1

Set out below are the chances (or the probabilities) of the distributions of falls when 3, 4, 5, 6, 7, 8, 9, and 10 coins are simultaneously tossed.

Distribution of chances of falls
3 coins

Chances in 8 Throws	3H	2H 1T	1H 2T	3T
	1	3	3	1

4 Coins

Chances in 16 Throws	4H	3H 1T	2H 2T	1H 3T	4T
	1	4	6	4	1

5 Coins

Chances in 32 Throws	5H	4H 1T	3H 2T	2H 3T	1H 4T	5T
	1	5	10	10	5	1

6 Coins

Chances in 64 Throws	6H	5H 1T	4H 2T	3H 3T	2H 4T	1H 5T	6T
	1	6	15	20	15	6	1

7 Coins

Chances in 128 Throws	7H	6H 1T	5H 2T	4H 3T	3H 4T	2H 5T	1H 6T	7T
	1	7	21	35	35	21	7	1

8 Coins

Chances in 256 Throws	8H	7H 1T	6H 2T	5H 3T	4H 4T	3H 5T	2H 6T	1H 7T	8T
	1	8	28	56	70	56	28	8	1

9 Coins

Chances in 512 Throws	9H	8H 1T	7H 2T	6H 3T	5H 4T	4H 5T	3H 6T	2H 7T	1H 8T	9T
	1	9	36	84	126	126	84	36	9	1

10 Coins

Chances in 1,024 Throws	10H	9H 1T	8H 2T	7H 3T	6H 4T	5H 5T	4H 6T	3H 7T	2H 8T	1H 9T	10T
	1	10	45	120	210	252	210	120	45	10	1

Look at the distribution of chances of falls for ten pennies. The chances of throwing five heads and five tails are 252 out of 1,024, that is, approximately one in four chances. The chances of throwing ten heads or ten tails are only one in over a thousand!

But what possible relevance have the distributions of tossed pennies to everyday matters?

5.14   A Practical Application of the Normal Probability Curve

For illustrative purposes only, the histogram below represents the numbers of pairs of men's shoes of varying sizes carried by a shoe shop. The average size in men's shoes is size eight. Our hypothetical shop owner (albeit intuitively) has correctly applied some awareness of the normal probability curve to his stock request order. The chances of customers with size three or size thirteen feet visiting his premises are sufficiently low as to deter him from keeping all but a few outsize shoes!

Figure 10   Hypothetical distribution of men's shoe sizes in stock.

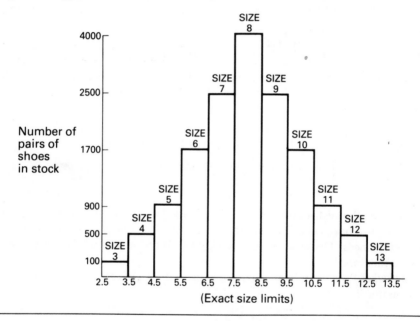

(Exact size limits)

Histograms drawn to represent such diverse properties as height, weight, intelligence quotients, and achievement test scores would be similar in shape to the one above illustrating the distribution of men's shoe sizes.

Suppose we were to construct such a histogram in respect of children's weight and that we were to use very fine gradations in weight (fractions of grams) in plotting the distribution of weight for 10,000 children. The effect of using very small weight categories over a very large population of children would be to transform the small step-like sides of the histogram into a smooth continuous curve: the normal curve of distribution.

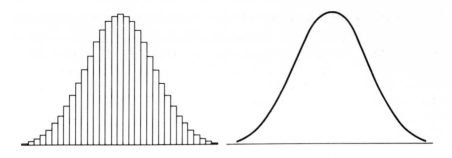

5.15 Some Mathematical Characteristics of the Normal Probability Curve

On the normal curve of distribution there are two points, called *points of inflection* where the curve changes direction from convex to concave. If a perpendicular line is dropped from these points of inflection to the base line (see diagram below) it is possible to measure off one *unit of distance* from either side of the central axis of the normal curve marked by the dotted line *X Y*.

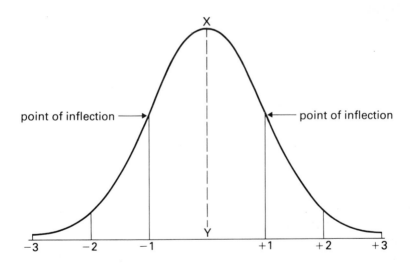

Statistics for Education and Physical Education

This unit of distance can be used as a *standard* by which to divide the base line into equal segments.

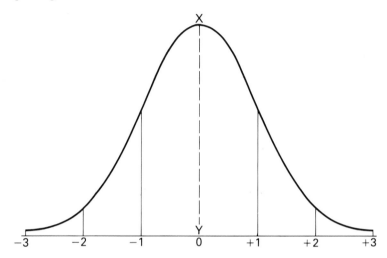

Each segment is *one standard unit of distance* or *one standard deviation* from the central axis *X Y*.

If we let the total area under the normal curve equal 100%, then one of the mathematical properties of the normal curve is that the area bounded by one standard deviation on either side of the central axis (or mean) is approximately 68.26% of the total area.

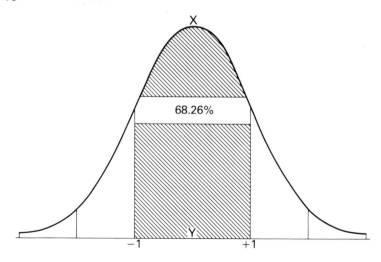

Suppose that in our hypothetical example of the shoe shop, the average man's shoe size is size eight (represented by the central axis or mean, XY). Suppose further that the standard unit of distance from the mean is two shoe sizes. Our shop owner would know that approximately 68% of his potential customers would require shoes of sizes six to ten.

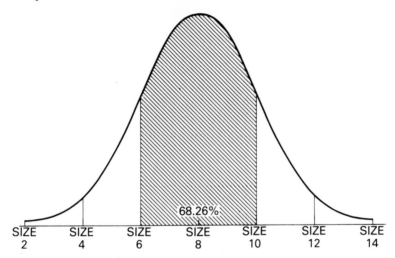

SIZE 2	SIZE 4	SIZE 6	SIZE 8	SIZE 10	SIZE 12	SIZE 14

68.26%

Given the hypothetical distribution of male foot sizes we can estimate from the diagram below the probability of the shoe-shop owner encountering customers with outsize feet!

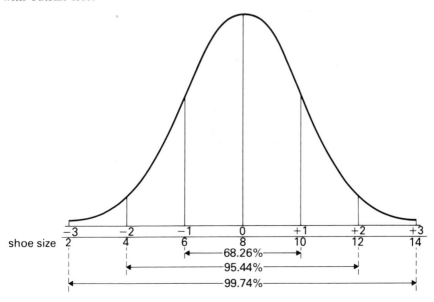

Statistics for Education and Physical Education

99.74% of men have shoe sizes between two and fourteen. The chances of a customer requesting size two or size fourteen shoes is about 1 in 300. The shop owner can complete his stock order with this knowledge in mind.

So far, we have described characteristics of normal probability curves where we have shown perfectly symmetrical balances between both sides of distributions as illustrated in Figures 9 and 10. In such curves, the three averages discussed earlier, the *mean*, the *median*, and the *mode*, all coincide.

Most data collected in Education and Physical Education however are not normally distributed. In Figures 11 and 12 below, we show two non-normal distributions commonly encountered by the researcher. We indicate the typical positions of the mean, median, and mode in these distributions.

Figure 11 shows a *negatively-skewed distribution,* that is, *skewed to the left.* Such a distribution might be found on a simple arithmetic test in which the majority of pupils in a class do well and only a few children fail to grasp the particular computational concepts.

Figure 11

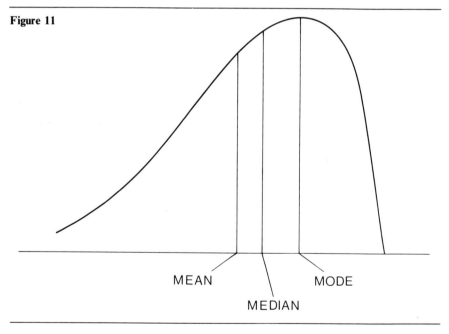

MEAN   MODE

MEDIAN

Figure 12 shows a *positively-skewed distribution,* that is, *skewed to the right.* Such a distribution might be found on a very difficult test where only a small number of pupils have a thorough grasp of the material whilst most of their fellows perform poorly.

Figure 12

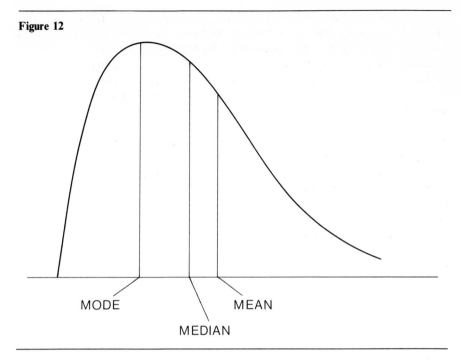

Notice how, in Figures 11 and 12, the mean tends to be 'pulled' away from the mode in the direction of extreme values.

Measuring Variations in Achievement

6.1 Introduction

The measures of central tendency outlined in Sections 5.1 to 5.11 describe the typical achievement of a group. They tell us nothing however, of the way in which individuals within the group differ from one another in their achievement. To know how individuals vary, we need measures of variability.

Variability refers to the extent to which individuals or scores differ from each other. As we shall see, certain measures of central tendency and of variability, when used together, enable us to compute precisely how different the achievements of two or more groups are.

6.2 The Range

The range is the simplest measure of variability. It tells us about the interval between the highest and the lowest scores in a distribution. The range shows how wide the distribution is over which our scores are spread. It is computed by taking the lowest from the highest score and adding 1. The addition of 1 allows for the exact limits of the lowest and highest scores in the range. In the distribution 2, 4, 5, 7, 7, 8, 9, the range is $9 - 2 + 1 = 8$. Because the range takes account only of the two most extreme scores, it is limited in its usefulness since it gives no information on how the scores are distributed.

Look at the following distributions. Whilst each has a range of 50, the distribution of the scores across the interval varies considerably.

$$3, \quad 9, \quad 16, \quad 28, \quad 35, \quad 43, \quad 52, \qquad \text{Range} = 50$$
$$11, \quad 20, \quad 21, \quad 22, \quad 23, \quad 25, \quad 60. \qquad \text{Range} = 50$$

Use the range when scores are too scattered to warrant the calculation of a more precise measure of variability, or when all that is required is knowledge of the overall spread of the scores.

6.3 Average Deviation (A.D.)

In discussing the Normal Curve in Section 5.14 we introduced the idea of units of distance which are measured off on either side of the central axis or mean of the bell-shaped curve. A unit of distance or a *deviation* from the mean helps describe the spread of the curve. That is to say, it provides an index of the amount of dispersion of the scores of a group about the mean. A deviation is simply the distance any score is from the mean of its distribution. Scores that are higher than the mean deviate positively, scores that are lower than the mean deviate negatively. If d = the deviation of a score, then the formula for calculating the deviation of any score (X) from the mean of its distribution (M) is given as:

$$d = X - M$$

Because scores are spread positively and negatively around the mean of any distribution, the true average deviation will always be zero. A *'true' average deviation* tells us nothing about the distribution. Therefore, to calculate the *average deviation* (note the difference!) we proceed as follows:

1 Ignore the signs attached to deviation (d) of each score. (The symbol $|d|$ means the *absolute value* of d, that is without signs.)

2 Add up or sum $(\sum)$ the d's.

3 Divide by N – the number of scores in the distribution.

The formula for the average deviation (A.D.) is given as:

$$\text{A.D.} = \frac{\sum |d|}{N}$$

The distribution 2, 3, 5, 6, 7, 8, 8, 9, has a mean of 6. The scores and their deviations are set out in Table 10.

Table 10   Calculating the Average Deviation

X	d
9	3
8	2
8	2
7	1
6	0
5	−1
3	−3
2	−4

$$\text{A.D.} = \frac{\sum |d|}{N} = \frac{16}{8} = 2$$

Notice how the *average deviation* improves upon the *range* as a measure of variability in that it takes account of all the scores in a distribution.

6.4   The Standard Deviation (S.D.)

Although the average deviation (A.D.) is rarely used in modern statistics, it has been included here as a useful introduction to the concept of deviation. Moreover, it leads directly into a consideration of the most commonly-used measure of variability, the *standard deviation* (S.D.).

How does the average deviation (A.D.) differ from the standard deviation (S.D.)? Recall that in discussing the Normal Curve in Section 5.14 we identified, not a 'unit of distance', but a '*standard unit of distance*' which we equated with '*standard deviation*'. Furthermore, we showed how that standard deviation was derived from the shape of the Normal Curve, to be precise, from the points of inflection, that is, where the curve changed direction from convex to concave. A mathematical explanation of how a standard deviation (as contrasted with an average deviation) is derived from the characteristics of the Normal Curve need not concern us here. At a more practical level, the immediate difference between the average deviation and the standard deviation is that in calculating A.D., we ignore all signs attached to *d*'s and sum their absolute values. In computing S.D.,

53

the difficulty of signs is by-passed. We simply square each of the deviations as the following examples show.

The following symbols will be used:

S.D. = the standard deviation

X = the raw score

M = the mean

d = the deviation score obtained by subtracting the mean from each raw score

d^2 = the deviation score squared

N = the number of cases

f = the frequency of a score

i = the class interval

C^i = the correction factor in terms of class intervals

6.5 Calculating the Standard Deviation from Ungrouped Data

The formula for the standard deviation from ungrouped data* is given as:

$$\text{S.D.} = \sqrt{\frac{\sum d^2}{N - 1}}$$

Example The raw scores of 11 boys on an Arithmetic test are arranged in descending order in Table 11 below.

1 First calculate M, the mean score, by dividing $\sum X$, the total of the raw scores by N, the number of cases.

$$M = \frac{\sum X}{N} = \frac{110}{11} = 10.0$$

2 Calculate d, the deviation score by subtracting M, the mean score from each raw score X. Enter the d score in the column next to the appropriate X score.

---

* Why $N - 1$ in the formula? One of the most easily understood explanations of the division by $N - 1$ is given in M. Hamburg (1974) *Basic Statistics: A Modern Approach*, New York: Harcourt, Brace Jovanovitch, page 64. In brief, when N is large, the subtraction of 1 is neither here nor there. With smaller N's however, $N - 1$ gives us a less-biased estimate of what the variance is in the population from which the particular sample is drawn.

Table 11   Calculating the Standard Deviation

X	d	d^2
16	6	36
14	4	16
12	2	4
11	1	1
10	0	0
10	0	0
9	−1	1
9	−1	1
8	−2	4
6	−4	16
5	−5	25
$\sum X = 110$	$\sum d = 0.0$	$\sum d^2 = 104$

3 Square each deviation score and enter in the third column. Note that in squaring *minus* quantities we obtain *plus* products. Sum the squared deviations.

4 Obtain S.D., the standard deviation, by extracting the square root of the sum of the square deviations divided by $N - 1$

$$\text{S.D.} = \sqrt{\frac{\sum d^2}{N-1}} \quad \text{In our example, S.D.} = \sqrt{\frac{104}{10}} = 3.2$$

6.6   Calculating the Standard Deviation from Grouped Data

Alternative formulae for calculating the standard deviation from grouped data are now given. The reader will see that the second of these formulae closely parallels the short method of computing the mean from grouped data outlined in Section 5.4 above.

Formula 1

$$\text{S.D.} = \sqrt{\frac{\sum fd^2}{N-1}}$$

The same data as in Table 11 are used.

Table 12   Calculating the Standard Deviation from Grouped Data (Formula 1)

X	f	fX	d	d^2	fd^2
16	1	16	6	36	36
14	1	14	4	16	16
12	1	12	2	4	4
11	1	11	1	1	1
10	2	20	0	0	0
9	2	18	-1	1	2
8	1	8	-2	4	4
6	1	6	-4	16	16
5	1	5	-5	25	25
	$N = 11$	$\sum fX = 110$			$\sum fd^2 = 104$
		$M = 10$			

$$\text{S.D.} = \sqrt{\frac{\sum fd^2}{N - 1}} \quad \text{In our example, S.D.} = \sqrt{\frac{104}{10}} = 3.2$$

Formula 2

$$\text{S.D.} = i \sqrt{\frac{\sum fd^2}{N - 1} - C^{i2}}$$

The same data as in Table 11 are used.

Table 13   Calculating the Standard Deviation from Grouped Data (Formula 2)

Score intervals	f	d	fd	fd^2
14–16	2	$+2$	$+4$	8
11–13	2	$+1$	$+2(+6)$	2
A.M. → 8–10	5	0		
5–7	2	-1	$-2(-2)$	2
	$N = 11$		$\sum fd = 4$	$\sum fd^2 = 12$

1 In Table 13, in the column headed d, we have placed the value 0 next to the interval containing our assumed mean (A.M.) and have assigned deviation values $+2$, $+1$, -1, as in the computation of the mean for grouped data in Section 5.4.

2 We obtain C^i, a correction factor in class interval units.

$$C^i = \frac{\sum fd}{N} = \frac{4}{11} = 0.36$$

This is squared to give $C^{i2} = 0.13$

3 We obtain $\sum fd^2$ by summing the values in column fd^2

$$\sum fd^2 = 12$$

$$\text{S.D.} = i \sqrt{\frac{\sum fd^2}{N-1} - C^{i2}} = 3\sqrt{\frac{12}{10} - 0.13} = 3\sqrt{1.07} = 3.1$$

6.7 Variance

Another measure of variability closely related to the standard deviation is the *variance*. Like the S.D., the variance is related to the size of the difference between each score and the mean of a distribution. The variance is simply the standard deviation squared.

$$\text{Variance} = \text{S.D.}^2 = \frac{\sum d^2}{N-1}$$

It's more common to use the S.D. than the variance in describing the variability of a distribution. Why bother computing the variance in that case? The variance, as we shall see, is used in many of the more advanced statistical analyses that we describe in the second part of the text.

6.8 Coefficient of Variation (V)

Recall that in our discussion of levels of measurement in Section 3.5 we described the ratio scale as the highest level of measurement and went on to illustrate a ratio scale by reference to weight.

In Physical Education where ratio scales are frequently used, researchers are often interested in the variability of a sample on one characteristic as compared with another. For example, does a sample of adolescent girls vary as much in height as in weight?

We cannot, of course, compare height and weight directly. But we can compare the relative variability of the group over its distribution on height and on weight. The *coefficient of variation* (*V*), sometimes known as the *coefficient of relative variation*, is the statistic we employ.

In computing V, we make use of the mean and the standard deviation of a distribution. In our hypothetical example since we are dealing with a sample, it is M_s, the mean of a sample that we use.

The formula for the coefficient of variation is given as:

$$V = \frac{100 \text{ S.D.}}{M_s} \%$$

Example In a sample of adolescent girls, the mean height is 1.5 metres with a standard deviation of 20 cms., and the mean weight is 50 kilograms with a standard deviation of 15 kilograms. On which characteristic is the group the more variable?

$$V_{\text{height}} = \frac{100 \times 20}{150} = \frac{2000}{150} = 13.3\%$$

$$V_{\text{weight}} = \frac{100 \times 15}{50} = \frac{1500}{50} = 30.0\%$$

This sample of adolescent girls is more than twice as variable in weight as in height.

6.9 The Quartile Deviation (*Q*)

Whenever the median is chosen as an appropriate measure of central tendency, then the quartile deviation is an appropriate measure of variability. Let's see why.

We need first to introduce the *percentile*. Percentiles are used to describe the position of a score in a distribution. Percentiles divide up a distribution into 100 parts. The 10th, the 20th, and the 30th percentiles are those scale values below which 10%, 20%, and 30% of the cases in a distribution fall.

The 50th percentile, written as P_{50}, indicates that this particular scale value has 50% of the total distribution above and below it. P_{50} is, of course, the median.

Quartiles divide up a distribution into 4 parts. Thus, the first quartile (Q_1) is the same as P_{25}, and the third quartile (Q_3) is the same as P_{75}.

The *quartile deviation* or Q is defined as one half the scale distance between the 75th and the 25th percentiles in a frequency distribution.

The formula for Q is given as:

$$Q = \frac{Q_3 - Q_1}{2}$$

It will be seen that the quartile deviation is simply a restricted version of the range; it tells us about the variability around the middle of a distribution of scores, that is, about the median.

Calculating Q

Example   The scores of 40 children on a reading comprehension test are set out in the frequency distribution in Table 14.

Table 14   Calculating the Quartile Deviation

Class interval	f	
85–89	1	count downwards for Q_3
80–84	1	
75–79	1	
70–74	2	
65–69	3	8 cases
60–64	4	
55–59	6	
50–54	7	
45–49	5	
40–44	3	10 cases
35–39	3	
30–34	2	
25–29	1	
20–24	1	count upwards for Q_1

$$N = 40$$

To calculate the quartile deviation we must first compute Q_1 and Q_3.

1 $Q_1 = P_{25}$. That is, 25% of the total number of cases (40) or *10 cases*. We begin to count upwards from the bottom of the frequency distribution. It can be seen that below the lower limit of the interval 45–49 (i.e. at 44.5) we have included exactly 10 cases. We have no need therefore to interpolate.

$Q_1 = 44.5$

2 $Q_3 = P_{75}$. We need not count upwards however. It's simpler to count downwards from the top of the frequency distribution. It can be seen that by the lower limit of the interval 65–69 (i.e. at 64.5) we have included 8 cases. We need to include 2 more. In the interval below the one containing the 8 cases (i.e. 60–64) there are 4 cases. We need to go down a further $\frac{2}{4}$ of the way through this interval. Arithmetically this is,

$Q_3 = 64.5 - \frac{2}{4}(5)$

$Q_3 = 64.5 - 2.5$

$Q_3 = 62.0$

3 To compute Q we proceed as follows:

$$Q = \frac{Q_3 - Q_1}{2} = \frac{62.0 - 44.5}{2} = \frac{17.5}{2} = 8.75(8.8)$$

6.10 The Usefulness of Q

The usefulness of Q as a measure of variability lies in the fact that one quartile deviation on either side of the median in a normal distribution contains 50% of the cases. In our example in Table 14 (near-normally distributed) the median is 53.1 (see Section 5.6 for the calculation of the median from grouped data). Thus 50% of the cases lie between $53.1 - 8.8$ and $53.1 + 8.8$, that is between 44.3 and 61.9.

Measuring Relative Achievement

7.1 Introduction

Often in Education and Physical Education we are concerned with interpreting and comparing individual scores. For example, we may wish to know whether a student's score is good or bad, whether he does better on Test A than on Test B, and how much better or worse his score is when compared with others in his group.

In order to interpret a particular test score correctly, we need to have a basis for comparison. This can be achieved by measuring the *relative standing* of the score in relation to the total distribution of scores for the group. Various methods are available for measuring the relative standing of a score. Two of the more commonly-used are discussed below.

7.2 Percentiles

A frequently-used measure of relative standing is the *percentile rank* (*p*). The percentile rank indicates the percentage of scores in a distribution that lie below any particular score. That specific score is known as the *percentile point*, designated (*P*).

For example, if a student scores 45 on a performance test and his percentile rank is calculated to be 70, then 70% of the total distribution of scores would lie below the score of 45. We can express the score 45 as P_{70} that is, 45 corresponds with the percentile rank, 70. Recall that in discussing the quartile deviation we noted that P_{50}, the 50th percentile, is that scale value which has 50% of the total distribution above and below it; in other words, P_{50} is the median.

The advantages of using percentile ranks as measures of relative standing are obvious. Not only can we compare an individual with other members of his group on a particular test, but an individual's performance on different tests can readily be evaluated – a percentile rank of 55 on Test A for example, being clearly superior to a percentile rank 50 on Test B.

There are two approaches to calculating percentiles. The first involves calculating the percentile points which correspond to particular percentile ranks. For example, what are the exact scores, (the percentile points) needed to achieve, say, the percentile ranks of 30 and 60?

The second approach involves calculating the percentile rank for a particular score.

7.3   Method 1: Calculating Percentile Points

The method employed in calculating percentile points is a modified form of that used in calculating the median (see page 37).

Example   Using the frequency distribution of sit up scores from page 37, calculate the scores corresponding to percentile ranks 10, 20, 30, 40, 50, 60, 70, 80, and 90.

Table 15   Calculating Percentile Points (Method 1)

Step intervals (rounded off)	Step intervals (exact limits)	f	cf
48–50	47.5–50.5	2	50
45–47	44.5–47.5	3	48
42–44	41.5–44.5	4	45
39–41	38.5–41.5	6	41
36–38	35.5–38.5	8	35
33–35	32.5–35.5	8	27
30–32	29.5–32.5	7	19
27–29	26.5–29.5	6	12
24–26	23.5–26.5	3	6
21–23	20.5–23.5	2	3
18–20	17.5–20.5	1	1

For Percentile Rank 10.

1 Construct a cumulative frequency column (cf), by serially adding the frequencies.

2 Multiply the desired percentile rank (10) by the total number of scores (50) and divide by 100.

$$\frac{p \times N}{100} = \frac{10 \times 50}{100} = 5$$

N.B. 10% of 50 = 5 or 5th score.

3 Moving up the cumulative frequency column note the step interval in which the 5th score lies (23.5–26.5)

Lower limit (L) = 23.5

4 Note the number of scores in the step interval in which the 5th score lies (f)

$f = 3$

5 Note the number of scores below that particular step interval (3).

6 Substitute into the formula:

$$P_p = L + \left(\frac{\frac{pN}{100} - S}{f} \times i\right)$$

where P_p = Percentile point for given percentile rank p
         p = Percentile rank desired (10)
         L = Lower limit of interval in which the P_p lies (23.5)
         N = Total number of scores (50)
         S = Sum of all the scores below L (3)
         f = Number of scores within the interval containing P_p (3)
         i = Step interval size (3)

$$P_{10} = 23.5 + \left(\frac{\frac{10 \times 50}{100} - 3}{3} \times 3\right)$$

$$= 23.5 + 2 = 25.5$$

$P_{10} = 25.5$ sit ups

It follows that 10% of the scores lie below score 25.5.

7 Repeat procedure for P_{20}, P_{30}, P_{40}, P_{50}, P_{60}, P_{70}, P_{80}, and P_{90}.

Table 16 Summary Table

Percentile rank	Calculation	Percentile point (P_p) (sit ups)
10	$23.5 + \left(\dfrac{\dfrac{10 \times 50}{100} - 3}{3} \times 3 \right)$	$P_{10} = 25.5$
20	$26.5 + \left(\dfrac{10 - 6}{6} \times 3 \right)$	$P_{20} = 28.5$
30	$29.5 + \left(\dfrac{15 - 12}{7} \times 3 \right)$	$P_{30} = 30.8$
40	$32.5 + \left(\dfrac{20 - 19}{8} \times 3 \right)$	$P_{40} = 32.87$
50	$32.5 + \left(\dfrac{25 - 19}{8} \times 3 \right)$	$P_{50} = 34.75$
60	$35.5 + \left(\dfrac{30 - 27}{8} \times 3 \right)$	$P_{60} = 36.62$
70	$38.5 + \left(\dfrac{35 - 35}{6} \times 3 \right)$	$P_{70} = 38.5$
80	$38.5 + \left(\dfrac{40 - 35}{6} \times 3 \right)$	$P_{80} = 41.0$
90	$44.5 + \left(\dfrac{45 - 45}{3} \times 3 \right)$	$P_{90} = 44.5$

7.4 Method 2: Calculating Percentile Ranks for Individual Scores

The procedure for computing percentile ranks for individual scores is basically the reverse of that outlined above.

Example Calculate the percentile rank (p) for score 34 (P_p) in the distribution of sit ups.

We are required to calculate p when $P_p = 34$. The formula we employ is as follows:

$$p = \frac{\left(\dfrac{f}{i}\right) \times (P_p - L) + S}{N} \times 100$$

The symbols have the same meaning as given on page 63, substituting from Table 15.

$$p = \frac{\frac{8}{3} \times (34 - 32.5) + 19}{50} \times 100$$

$$= 46 \text{ (Rounded off)}$$

A score of 34 has a percentile rank of 46. That is to say, 46% of the scores lie below score 34.

We can see from the preceding sections that a percentile rank provides us with an indication of relative position within a group. At times, however, this can be misleading. Take, for example, the Percentile Rank Summary Table (Table 16). In that table we note that to achieve percentile rank 10, an individual needs to obtain a percentile point score of 25.5 sit ups. To achieve percentile rank 20, he needs a percentile point score of 28.5 sit ups. In other words a difference of 3 sit ups moves him up 10 ranks. Now consider ranks 40 and 50 in the same table. A difference of 1.88 sit ups (34.75 − 32.87) is sufficient to move an individual the 10 ranks from 40 to 50.

Consider also the following hypothetical results of two tests performed by each of four individuals.

Table 17   Hypothetical Test Results for Four Individuals

	TEST A Marks out of 100	TEST B Marks out of 100
John	95	95
Mary	25	93
Sue	20	92
Peter	19	19

If the percentile ranks were calculated they would be the same on both tests for each of the four individuals. The distributions of raw scores within each test however are quite different. In Test A, John scores far better than all others, whereas in Test B, John, Mary, and Sue all score very much alike and obtain far higher marks than Peter.

The lesson is plain. Percentiles can provide us with a measure of rank only, *not* a measure of difference between scores.

If a more accurate and meaningful picture of relative achievement is required, we must take into account not only the ranking of scores but also the differences between them, that is, their variability. We can do this by using measures of relative achievement known as standard scores.

7.5   Standard Scores or *Z* Scores

A standard score or *Z* score tells us where any particular score lies in relation to the mean score of its distribution. Not only does a standard score indicate whether a particular score lies above or below the mean; it shows how far above or below the mean that score is located.

Before showing how to calculate standard scores it is important that the reader has a thorough grasp of the rationale behind them.

Let's reconsider the mathematical properties of a normal curve that we touched upon in Section 5.14.

Recall that one of the properties of a normal curve is that a score can be placed above or below the mean of a distribution in terms of a standard unit of distance and that the percentage of scores above or below that score can be estimated.

The hypothetical example we provided in our discussion of the normal curve was to do with shoe sizes. We showed how shoe sizes could be described in terms of standard deviations from the mean.

In Figure 13 below, we see that the average shoe size is 8 and that shoe size 10 is one standard deviation, that is, two shoe sizes above the mean. Size 12 is two standard deviations or four shoe sizes above the mean.

It follows that shoe size 9 is 0.5 standard deviations or 1 shoe size above the mean.

Our example shows that if we position scores in standard deviation units above or below the mean of a normal distribution, then not only do we get a measure of rank, but also a standard measure of the distance between the scores. The difference between a score one standard deviation above the mean and a score two standard deviations above the mean is the same as the difference between a score three standard deviations above the mean and one at two standard deviations above the mean.

The distance a score lies above or below the mean of a distribution, measured in standard deviation units, is called its *standard score* or *z score*.

Figure 13 Shoe sizes shown as standard deviations from the mean.

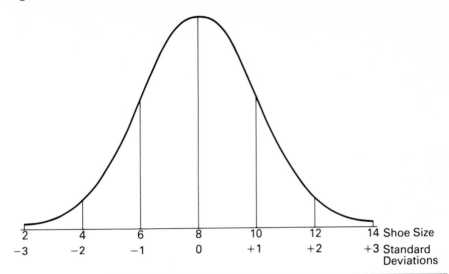

If we convert actual raw scores into standard scores we obtain an accurate picture of that score's relative position in a distribution.

To convert a raw score into a standard score we need first to calculate the mean and the standard deviation of the distribution. Both these procedures are outlined in Sections 5.2 and 6.4. The mean and standard deviation are then substituted into the formula:

$$Z = \frac{X - M}{\text{S.D.}}$$

where Z = standard score
              X = raw score
              M = mean
       S.D. = standard deviation.

7.6 Example 1

The mean score on a spelling test is 50 and the standard deviation is 10. What is the standard score for John who scores 65? (Assume a normal distribution.)

$$Z = \frac{X - M}{\text{S.D.}}$$

$$Z = \frac{65 - 50}{10} = +1.5$$

John's score is 1.5 standard deviations above the mean. It can be represented diagrammatically as:

Figure 14 Standard score diagram of Example 1.

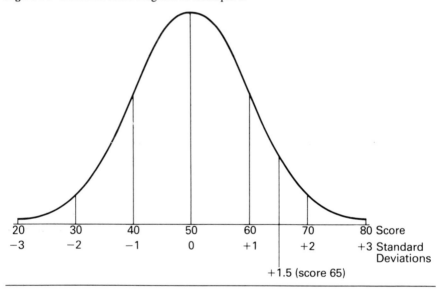

Scores can, of course, have negative Z values. All those scores below the mean have negative Z values. All those above the mean, positive Z values.

7.7 Example 2

As part of a physical fitness assessment, a group of students is tested on strength, speed, and balance.

Given the following results for student K, and assuming normal distribution of results, on which test does that individual do best?

Table 18   Strength, Speed and Balance Scores

	Raw score	Mean	Standard deviation
Strength test	87	75	12
Speed test	16	13	2
Balance test	31	34	10

1   Calculate Z for Strength test

$$Z = \frac{X - M}{\text{S.D.}} = \frac{87 - 75}{12} = +1$$

2   Calculate Z for Speed test

$$Z = \frac{X - M}{\text{S.D.}} = \frac{16 - 13}{2} = +1.5$$

3   Calculate Z for Balance test

$$Z = \frac{X - M}{\text{S.D.}} = \frac{31 - 34}{10} = -0.3$$

Student K achieves better results on the speed test than on the strength or the balance tests, in as much as his Z score shows that he is further above the average for that test.

Student K's results can be represented diagrammatically:

Figure 15   Strength test data diagrammed.

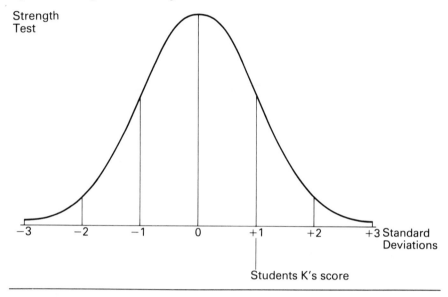

Figure 16   Speed test data diagrammed.

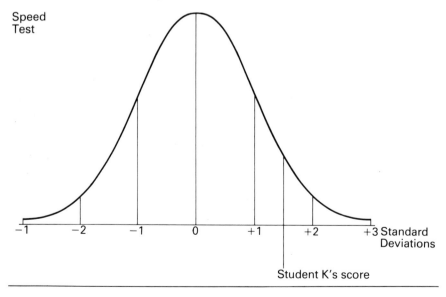

Figure 17 Balance test data diagrammed.

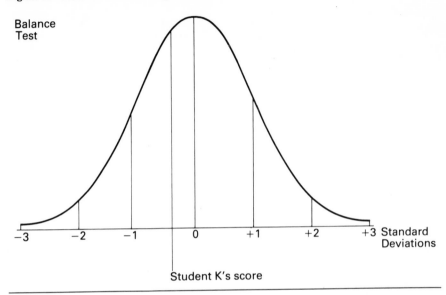

The examples above show how standard scores can be used to identify a score's position in relation to its distance from the mean. This is not the only information we can obtain about the relative standing of a score. If the distribution is normal, we can also estimate how many scores lie above or below our particular score.

From the properties of the normal curve we know that if the area under it is equal to 100%, then within one standard deviation on either side of the mean, 68.26% of scores lie, within two standard deviations lie 95.44% of scores, and within three standard deviations on either side of the mean lie 99.74% of scores (see Section 5.14).

When the distances of successive points from the mean of a normal distribution are known and are measured in standard deviation units it is possible to estimate the percentage of scores that lie between the mean and these various points. This information is usually given in the form of a table such as the one set out below.

Table 19   Percentage of Scores Under the Normal Curve from 0 to Z

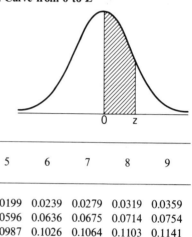

z	0	1	2	3	4	5	6	7	8	9
0.0	0.0000	0.0040	0.0080	0.0120	0.0160	0.0199	0.0239	0.0279	0.0319	0.0359
0.1	0.0398	0.0438	0.0478	0.0517	0.0557	0.0596	0.0636	0.0675	0.0714	0.0754
0.2	0.0793	0.0832	0.0871	0.0910	0.0948	0.0987	0.1026	0.1064	0.1103	0.1141
0.3	0.1179	0.1217	0.1255	0.1293	0.1331	0.1368	0.1406	0.1443	0.1480	0.1517
0.4	0.1554	0.1591	0.1628	0.1664	0.1700	0.1736	0.1772	0.1808	0.1844	0.1879
0.5	0.1915	0.1950	0.1985	0.2019	0.2054	0.2088	0.2123	0.2157	0.2190	0.2224
0.6	0.2258	0.2291	0.2324	0.2357	0.2389	0.2422	0.2454	0.2486	0.2518	0.2549
0.7	0.2580	0.2612	0.2642	0.2673	0.2704	0.2734	0.2764	0.2794	0.2823	0.2852
0.8	0.2881	0.2910	0.2939	0.2967	0.2996	0.3023	0.3051	0.3078	0.3106	0.3133
0.9	0.3159	0.3186	0.3212	0.3238	0.3264	0.3289	0.3315	0.3340	0.3365	0.3389
1.0	0.3413	0.3438	0.3461	0.3485	0.3508	0.3531	0.3554	0.3577	0.3599	0.3621
1.1	0.3643	0.3665	0.3686	0.3708	0.3729	0.3749	0.3770	0.3790	0.3810	0.3830
1.2	0.3849	0.3869	0.3888	0.3907	0.3925	0.3944	0.3962	0.3980	0.3997	0.4015
1.3	0.4032	00.4049	0.4066	0.4082	0.4099	0.4115	0.4131	0.4147	0.4162	0.4177
1.4	0.4192	0.4207	0.4222	0.4236	0.4251	0.4265	0.4279	0.4292	0.4306	0.4319
1.5	0.4332	0.4345	0.4357	0.4370	0.4382	0.4394	0.4406	0.4418	0.4429	0.4441
1.6	0.4452	0.4463	0.4474	0.4484	0.4495	0.4505	0.4515	0.4525	0.4535	0.4545
1.7	0.4554	0.4564	0.4573	0.4582	0.4591	0.4599	0.4608	0.4616	0.4625	0.4633
1.8	0.4641	0.4649	0.4656	0.4664	0.4671	0.4678	0.4686	0.4693	0.4699	0.4706
1.9	0.4713	0.4719	0.4726	0.4732	0.4738	0.4744	0.4750	0.4756	0.4761	0.4767

Table 19   Percentage of Scores Under the Normal Curve from 0 to Z (continued)

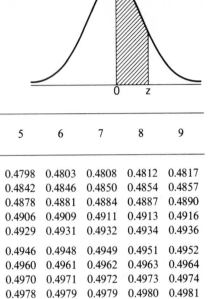

z	0	1	2	3	4	5	6	7	8	9
2.0	0.4772	0.4778	0.4783	0.4788	0.4793	0.4798	0.4803	0.4808	0.4812	0.4817
2.1	0.4821	0.4826	0.4830	0.4834	0.4838	0.4842	0.4846	0.4850	0.4854	0.4857
2.2	0.4861	0.4864	0.4868	0.4871	0.4875	0.4878	0.4881	0.4884	0.4887	0.4890
2.3	0.4893	0.4896	0.4898	0.4901	0.4904	0.4906	0.4909	0.4911	0.4913	0.4916
2.4	0.4918	0.4920	0.4922	0.4925	0.4927	0.4929	0.4931	0.4932	0.4934	0.4936
2.5	0.4938	0.4940	0.4941	0.4943	0.4945	0.4946	0.4948	0.4949	0.4951	0.4952
2.6	0.4953	0.4955	0.4956	0.4957	0.4959	0.4960	0.4961	0.4962	0.4963	0.4964
2.7	0.4965	0.4966	0.4967	0.4968	0.4969	0.4970	0.4971	0.4972	0.4973	0.4974
2.8	0.4974	0.4975	0.4976	0.4977	0.4977	0.4978	0.4979	0.4979	0.4980	0.4981
2.9	0.4981	0.4982	0.4982	0.4983	0.4984	0.4984	0.4985	0.4985	0.4986	0.4986
3.0	0.4987	0.4987	0.4987	0.4988	0.4988	0.4989	0.4989	0.4989	0.4990	0.4990
3.1	0.4990	0.4991	0.4991	0.4991	0.4992	0.4992	0.4992	0.4992	0.4993	0.4993
3.2	0.4993	0.4993	0.4994	0.4994	0.4994	0.4994	0.4994	0.4995	0.4995	0.4995
3.3	0.4995	0.4995	0.4995	0.4996	0.4996	0.4996	0.4996	0.4996	0.4996	0.4997
3.4	0.4997	0.4997	0.4997	0.4997	0.4997	0.4997	0.4997	0.4997	0.4997	0.4998
3.5	0.4998	0.4998	0.4998	0.4998	0.4998	0.4998	0.4998	0.4998	0.4998	0.4998
3.6	0.4998	0.4998	0.4999	0.4999	0.4999	0.4999	0.4999	0.4999	0.4999	0.4999
3.7	0.4999	0.4999	0.4999	0.4999	0.4999	0.4999	0.4999	0.4999	0.4999	0.4999
3.8	0.4999	0.4999	0.4999	0.4999	0.4999	0.4999	0.4999	0.4999	0.4999	0.4999
3.9	0.5000	0.5000	0.5000	0.5000	0.5000	0.5000	0.5000	0.5000	0.5000	0.5000

Once we have calculated a Z score we can estimate how many scores lie between the mean and our particular score. We do this by reference to Table 19.

Take, for example, a Z score of 0.8. By reference to Table 19 we see that 28.81% of the scores lie between a Z of 0.8 and the mean. We know also that 78.81% of all scores lie below our score. That is, 50.00% + 28.81% = 78.81% as shown in the figure below.

Figure 18   Percentage of scores under the normal curve (Example 1).

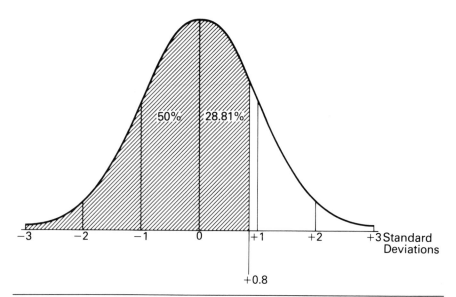

7.8   More Examples

2   Calculate the percentage of individuals who score below 32 when the mean of the distribution is 48 and the standard deviation is 10.

$$Z = \frac{32 - 48}{10} = -1.6$$

From Table 19 we see that 44.52% score between the mean and -1.6 S.D.'s (that is, score 32). It follows that $50.00\% - 44.52\% = 5.48\%$ of the scores lie below score 32. We diagram the calculation below in fig. 19.

3   If the mean of a distribution is 96 and the standard deviation is 28, what percentage of individuals scored above 110?

$$Z = \frac{110 - 96}{28} = \frac{14}{28} = +0.5$$

From Table 19 we see that 19.15% score between the mean and $+0.5$ S.D.'s (that is, score 110). If follows that $100\% - (50.00\% + 19.15\%) = 30.85\%$ of the scores lie above score 110. We diagram the calculation below in fig. 20.

Figure 19 Percentage of scores under the normal curve (Example 2).

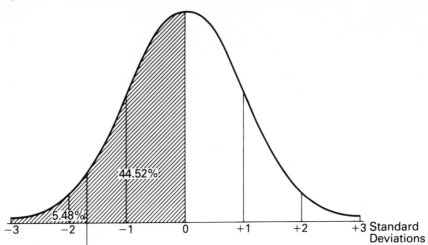

1.6 (score 32)

Figure 20 Percentage of scores under the normal curve (Example 3).

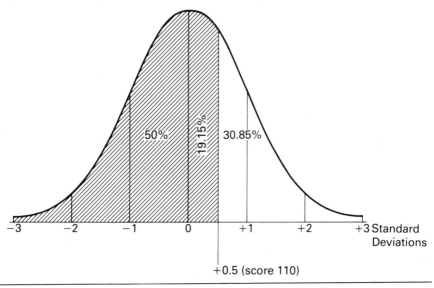

+0.5 (score 110)

4 If the mean of a distribution is 45 and the standard deviation is 5, what percentage of individuals score between 40 and 60?

Z for score 40

$$Z = \frac{40 - 45}{5} = -1$$

From Table 19 we see that 34.13% score between the mean and −1.0 S.D.'s (that is, score 40). We diagram this below.

Figure 21 Percentage of scores under the normal curve (Example 4.a).

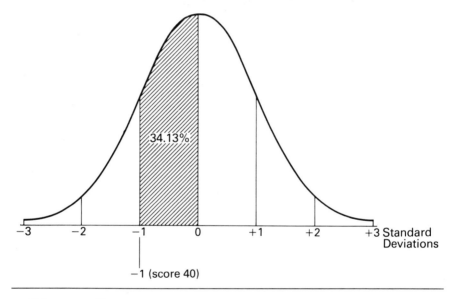

Z for score 60

$$Z = \frac{60 - 45}{5} = +3$$

From Table 19 we see that 49.87% score between the mean and +3.0 S.D.'s (that is, score 60). We diagram this below.

Figure 22 Percentage of scores under the normal curve (Example 4.b).

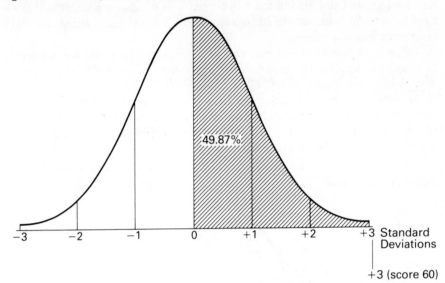

It follows that $34.13\% + 49.87\%$, that is, 84.00% of the scores lie between scores 40 and 60.

Figure 23 Percentage of scores under the normal curve (Example 4.c).

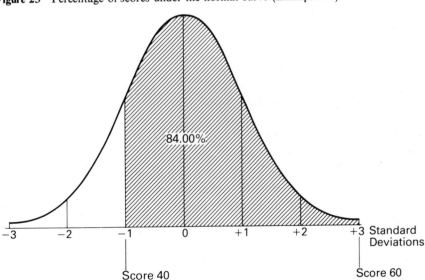

7.9 Sigma, Hull and *T* Scales

One problem in using standard scores as measures of relative position is that we have to work in standard deviation units which may be decimalized, and have positive or negative values.

This can be confusing and may lead to errors. One way round the problem is to transform the Z scores so as to arrive at a simple measure of relative position defined in points from 0 to 100.

To make this transformation we have to consider the normal distribution curve, not only in terms of standard deviation units above or below the mean, but as a series of points from 0 to 100 with a mean score set at 50 points. Such a transformation is called a *sigma scale*.

Figure 24 Sigma scale.

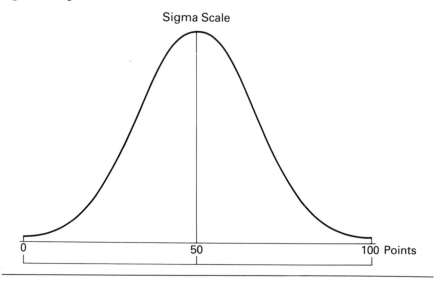

7.10 Sigma Scale

In the construction of a sigma scale the distribution curve is divided into 100 equal parts along its horizontal axis, commencing with the 0 at 3 standard deviations below the mean and finishing with the 100 at 3 standard deviations above the mean.

Figure 25 Sigma points and standard deviations.

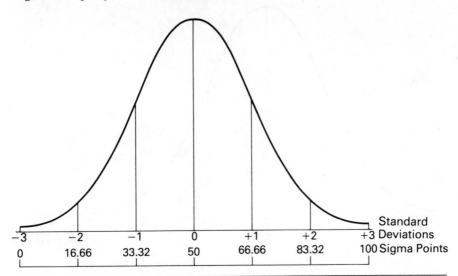

To calculate the sigma points for specific test score we use the formula:

Sigma points $= 16.66Z + 50$

where $Z = \dfrac{X - M}{S.D.}$

X = Raw score
M = Mean
S.D. = Standard Deviation

Example Using the data from Example 1 (page 68) we can calculate the points scored by John who gained 65 marks in a spelling test when the mean of the distribution was 50 and the standard deviation 10.

$$\text{Sigma points} = 16.66Z + 50 = 16.66\left(\frac{65 - 50}{10}\right) + 50$$

$$= 24.99 + 50$$

$$= 74.99$$

John scores 74.99 sigma points for the spelling test.

Figure 26 Sigma points calculation diagrammed.

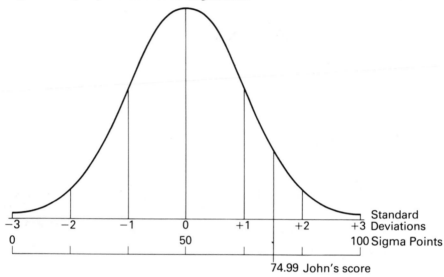

			Standard
−3	−2	−1	0	+1	+2	+3 Deviations

0   50   100 Sigma Points

74.99 John's score

7.11 The Hull Scale

The Hull Scale (named after its originator) is another way of transforming Z scores into a simpler measure of relative position defined in points from 0 to 100.

In the Hull Scale, we again divide the distribution curve into 100 equal parts, but this time the starting point (0) is positioned 3.5 standard deviations below the mean and the finishing point (100) 3.5 standard deviations above the mean.

To calculate Hull points for a particular test score we use the formula:

Hull points $= 14.28Z + 50$

where Z has its usual meaning.

Example Once again using John's mark of 65 in a spelling test when the mean is 50 and the standard deviation is 10 (see page 68), we can calculate how many Hull points he obtained.

$$\text{Hull points} = 14.28Z + 50 = 14.28 \left(\frac{65 - 50}{10} \right) + 50$$

$$= 21.42 + 50$$

$$= 71.42$$

John scores 71.42 Hull points on the spelling test.

Figure 27 Hull points and standard deviations.

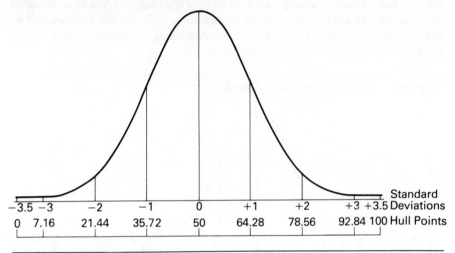

Figure 28 Hull points calculation diagrammed.

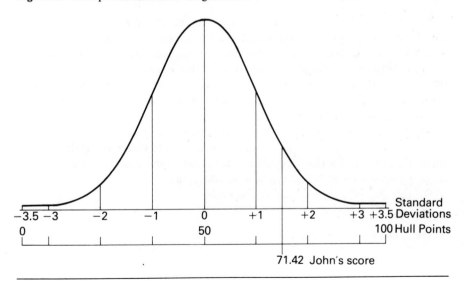

7.12 T-Scale

Yet another method of scaling which divides the distribution curve into 100 equal parts obtains an even greater spread of raw scores than in the Hull Scale. The starting point (0) is placed 5 standard deviations below the mean and the finishing point (100), 5 standard deviations above the mean.

Figure 29 *T*-points and standard deviations.

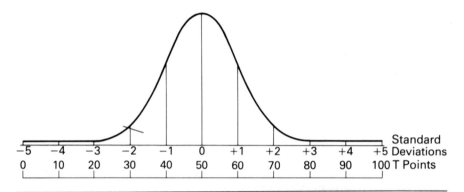

From our previous discussion we know that 99.74% of the scores in a normal distribution lie between ±3 standard deviations from the mean.

Looking at the diagram above, we can see that most raw scores will be given *T*-points between 20 and 80. It might appear that the outside ranges (0–20) and (80–100) are redundant. However the usefulness of the *T*-scale is demonstrated when there are extreme scores in a distribution, that is, scores that are more than 3 standard deviations from the mean.

In a sigma scale no points are made available within the range 0–100 for scores that lie outside ±3 standard deviations from the mean. Using a *T*-scale however, when a score is more than 3 standard deviations away from the mean a points score within the range 0–100 can still be allocated.

To calculate *T*-points we use the formula:

$$T\text{-points} = 10Z + 50$$

where Z has its usual meaning.

Example Referring again to John's spelling test mark of 65 when the distribution mean is 50 and standard deviation 10 we can estimate his *T*-points as follows:

$$T\text{-points} = 10Z + 50 = 10\left(\frac{65 - 50}{10}\right) + 50$$
$$= 15 + 50$$
$$= 65$$

John scores 65 *T*-points for the spelling test.

Figure 30 *T*-points calculation diagrammed.

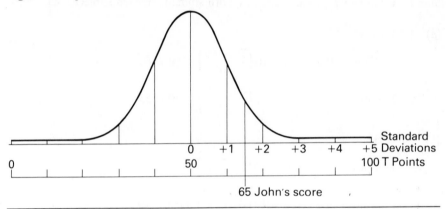

7.13 Example Problem

Given the following examination scores, calculate which student performed better overall. (Assume normal distribution.)

Table 20 Hypothetical Examination Scores for Two Individuals

	ENGLISH Mean = 60 S.D. = 10	MATHS. Mean = 55 S.D. = 12	FRENCH Mean = 50 S.D. = 5
Kim	70	31	60
Phillipa	65	43	53

First inspection of the above scores suggests that Kim (K) and Phillipa (P) did equally well, both scoring a total of 161 marks. This would be an incorrect conclusion however, as the distribution of marks for each subject area is different, that is, the means and standard deviations are different.

In order to compare the two sets of marks we must convert them into standardized units of measurement before adding. The relative position or achievement of each student in each subject area must be taken into account.

The standardization of marks can be achieved by methods already described earlier in the chapter. We shall use a T-scale.

Step 1 Calculate T-points gained by both students in each subject area.

(a) ENGLISH

K. $T\text{-points} = 10Z + 50 = 10\left(\dfrac{70 - 60}{10}\right) + 50 = 60$

P. $T\text{-points} = 10Z + 50 = 10\left(\dfrac{65 - 60}{10}\right) + 50 = 55$

(b) MATHS.

K. $T\text{-points} = 10Z + 50 = 10\left(\dfrac{31 - 55}{12}\right) + 50 = 30$

P. $T\text{-points} = 10Z + 50 = 10\left(\dfrac{43 - 55}{12}\right) + 50 = 40$

(c) FRENCH

K. $T\text{-points} = 10Z + 50 = 10\left(\dfrac{60 - 50}{5}\right) + 50 = 70$

P. $T\text{-points} = 10Z + 50 = 10\left(\dfrac{53 - 50}{5}\right) + 50 = 56$

Step 2 Total the T-points for each student

K. $= 60 + 30 + 70 = 160$

P. $= 55 + 40 + 56 = 151$

In relation to the overall distribution of scores for the whole examination, Kim achieved better results than Phillipa.

7.14 Grading

As well as considering individual performance in relation to that of the total group, we often categorize students into broad bands of achievement, giving those who score within a certain range of specific classification a grade. For example, after collecting test scores, we may wish to award students a grade of A, B, C, D, or E.

If we assume that the scores on our test are normally distributed, we may use the rationale behind the standardization of scores already outlined to construct a 5 grade scale.

First we must divide the distribution curve into 5 equal parts along the horizontal axis with the top of the A grade 3 standard deviations above the mean and the bottom of the E grade 3 standard deviations below the mean. That is, a six standard deviations range within which 99.74% of all the scores will lie.

Figure 31 Constructing a 5-grade scale.

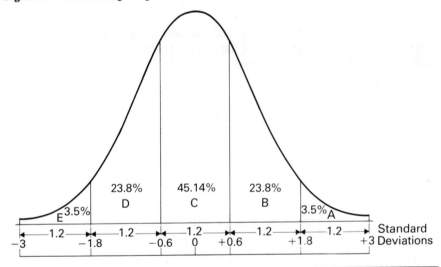

The range of each grade, that is, the difference between the upper and the lower limits, will be equal to 1.2 standard deviations (6 standard deviations divided by 5). However this information does not allow us to fix the actual positions of the grades since as yet we have no reference point. If we take the mean of the distribution as the reference point we can now place the limits of the grades accordingly.

A grade – Upper Limit = + 3.0 S.D.'s

Lower Limit = + 1.8 S.D.'s

B grade – Upper Limit = + 1.8 S.D.'s

Lower Limit = + 0.6 S.D.'s

C grade – Upper Limit = + 0.6 S.D.'s

Lower Limit = − 0.6 S.D.'s

D grade – Upper Limit = − 0.6 S.D.'s

Lower Limit = − 1.8 S.D.'s

E grade – Upper Limit = − 1.8 S.D.'s

Lower Limit = − 3.0 S.D.'s

Now we need only know the mean and standard deviation of our data in order to fix the upper and lower limits of the grades. The percentage of scores within each grade band can be estimated using Table 19.

7.15 Example

Suppose the mean of a distribution is 65 and the standard deviation 15. What are the limits of the grade bands?

A grade – Upper Limit = 65 + (3 × 15)   = 110

Lower Limit = 65 + (1.8 × 15) = 92

B grade – Upper Limit =   = 92

Lower Limit = 65 + (0.6 × 15) = 74

C grade – Upper Limit =   = 74

Lower Limit = 65 − (0.6 × 15) = 56

D grade – Upper Limit =   = 56

Lower Limit = 65 − (1.8 × 15) = 38

E grade – Upper Limit =   = 38

Lower Limit = 65 − (3 × 15)   = 20

Figure 32 Using a 5-grade scale (Example).

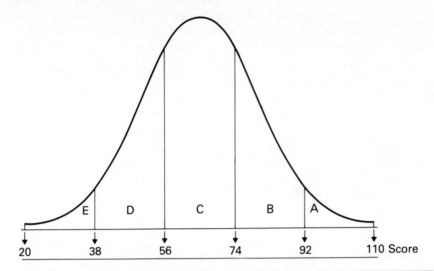

Depending upon particular requirements, this method can be applied to give any number of grade bands.

Measuring Relationships

8.1 Introduction

Many things that occur in nature are related; the amount of rainfall and the depth of rivers, the position of the sun and the temperature of the land. So too, in Education and Physical Education, many variables are related; intelligence and achievement, cardiovascular fitness and oxygen uptake. Relationships between variables are referred to as *correlations*.

When an increase in one variable is accompanied by an increase in another, the correlation is said to be *positive* or *direct*. Intelligence test scores and academic grades are positively or directly related. When an increase in one variable is accompanied by a decrease in another, the correlation is said to be *negative* or *inverse*. Age and short term memory are negatively or inversely related.

The fact that variables are related however, does not mean that one *causes* the other. Such may be the case but it does not necessarily follow. Take, for example, the two measures, *lung volume* and *high-jump ability*. It's quite absurd to suggest that one 'causes' the other; both, no doubt, are related to underlying variables such as age and height.

In everyday language the word 'correlation' describes any type of relationship between objects or events; in statistics, correlation has a precise meaning.

Correlation refers to a quantifiable relationship between two variables.

The statistic that provides an index of the degree or the extent to which two variables are related is called the *correlation coefficient*.

8.2 The Meaning of Statistical Correlation

One way of showing the relationship between two variables is by means of a *scatter diagram* or *scatterplot*.

A scatter diagram is simply a graph on which points are placed to represent pairs of values for two variables. Look at Table 21 showing the test results of ten pupils in four school examinations.

Table 21 Hypothetical Test Scores for Ten Pupils

Names	Arithmetic	English	Art	Chemistry
Bill	75	75	45	71
Jim	70	70	50	45
Mary	70	70	50	56
John	65	65	55	50
Fred	60	60	60	60
Sue	60	60	60	70
Anne	55	55	65	70
Ken	50	50	70	50
Kay	50	50	70	65
Jane	45	45	75	51

In scatter diagrams 1, 2, and 3 we have plotted pairs of values to show the relationship between scores in Arithmetic and English, English and Art, and English and Chemistry respectively.

It appears that in the Arithmetic and English tests, each individual scores an identical mark in both tests, a truly remarkable result rarely found outside of fictitious data such as ours. The scatter diagram shows a 'perfect' positive or direct correlation between the two sets of scores.

Figure 33 Scatter diagram (1).

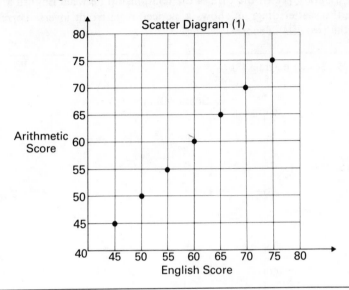

Figure 34 Scatter diagram (2).

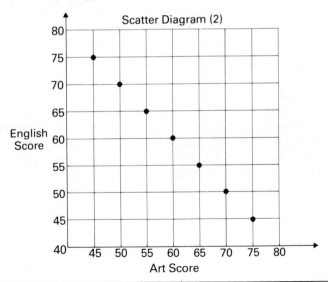

Equally surprising (and fictitious!) we have the very reverse of the picture in Scatter diagram (1). In the case of the relationship between English and Art test results, the scatter diagram shows a 'perfect' negative or inverse correlation between the two sets of scores.

Figure 35 Scatter diagram (3).

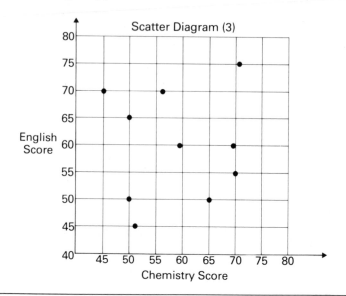

The reason for the term *Scatter* is well-illustrated when we plot the relationship between English and Chemistry test scores. Pupils who do well in English are just as likely to do well or badly in Chemistry. There is no obvious relationship between the two sets of scores. The scatter diagram shows a zero or near zero relationship. We may conclude that the two variables are independent.

In Education and Physical Education data, few variables are perfectly related to the degree shown in Scatter diagrams 1 and 2. Scatter diagrams 4, 5, 6, and 7 demonstrate the sorts of relationships more usually found. The data shown in these scatterplots are hypothetical and for illustrative purposes only. Notice in Scatter diagrams 4 and 5 that although the points do not fall along perfectly straight lines, lines are nevertheless apparent.

Figure 36 Scatter diagram (4).

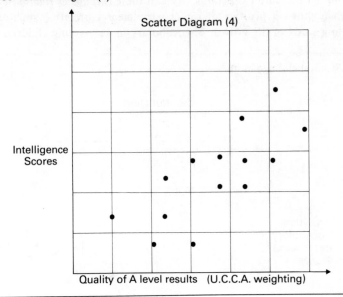

Figure 37 Scatter diagram (5).

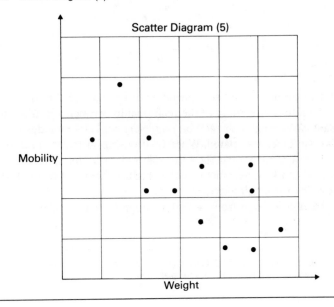

Sometimes relationships assume *curve-like* shapes rather than straight lines when plotted on scatter diagrams. We call these *curvilinear relationships*. Scatter diagram 6 shows a positive or direct curvilinear correlation such as might be found in a study of the growth of vocabulary in very young children.

Figure 38 Scatter diagram (6).

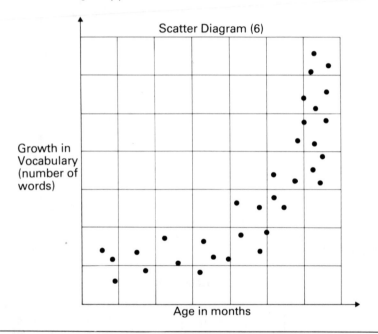

Scatter diagram 7 illustrates a negative or inverse curvilinear correlation such as might be found in a study of the relationship between age and rate of growth.

We said earlier that a *correlation coefficient* provides an index of the degree to which two variables are related. When relationships between variables can best be described by a straight line they are referred to as *linear relationships*. Linear relationships can be determined by the product moment* correlation coefficient, symbolized by the small letter, r.

The values of r range from $+1.00$, through 0.00, to -1.00.

---

* Why 'product-moment'? See H. E. Garrett (1960), *Statistics in Psychology and Education*, New York: Longmans Green, footnote page 127 for an explanation.

Figure 39 Scatter diagram (7).

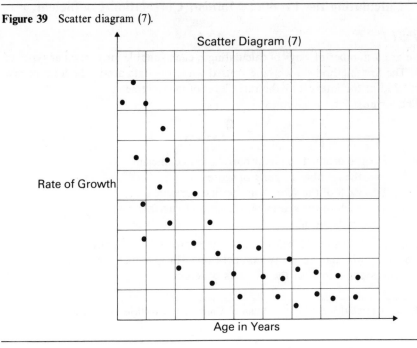

Look at Scatter diagram 1. If the points in that scatterplot are joined together, they form a straight line. The correlation shown in Scatter diagram 1 is a perfect positive or direct linear relationship of $+1.00$, that is, $r = 1.00$.

Look at Scatter diagram 2. If the points in that scatterplot are joined together they also form a straight line. The correlation shown in Scatter diagram 2 is a perfect negative or inverse linear relationship of -1.00, that is, $r = -1.00$.

Look at Scatter diagram 4. If we find the 'best fit' that a straight line can take with respect to all of the points in the scatterplot, it represents a strong positive or direct linear relationship, probably in the range 0.80 to 0.90. Similarly with Scatter diagram 5. A 'best fit' straight line representing a strong negative or inverse linear relationship would probably be in the range -0.60 to -0.70.

What of the curvilinear relationships shown in Scatter diagrams 6 and 7? Since a straight line 'best fit' is impossible in such circumstances, the product moment correlation coefficient, r, is inappropriate. What is needed is a correlation coefficient that can be applied whether the 'best fit' line is straight or curved. There is such a coefficient. It is called *eta* (η). The interested reader is referred to Downie and Heath (1974), pages 110–114, or to Wiseman (1966), pages 13–15, for a fuller discussion of the correlation coefficient *eta*.

8.3 Calculating the Product Moment Correlation Coefficient, r

Method 1

There are a number of ways of calculating r, each suitable for particular types of data. The first method shown here is used when the data are in the form of raw scores and at the interval or the ratio level of measurement.

The formula for r is given as:

$$r = \frac{n \sum XY - (\sum X)(\sum Y)}{\sqrt{[n \sum X^2 - (\sum X)^2][n \sum Y^2 - (\sum Y)^2]}}$$

where r = the product moment correlation coefficient
         n = the number of pairs of scores
         X = each of the scores on the first variable
         Y = each of the scores on the second variable
         $\sum$ = the 'sum of'.

The data in Table 22 below show the scores of ten pupils on two tests, a vocabulary quiz and an essay competition. The product moment correlation coefficient is computed for the two sets of scores.

Table 22   Calculating the Product Moment Correlation Coefficient (Method 1)

Vocabulary quiz X	Essay competition Y	X^2	Y^2	XY
43	4	1849	16	172
55	5	3025	25	275
67	6	4489	36	402
38	4	1444	16	152
49	5	2401	25	245
70	7	4900	49	490
80	9	6400	81	720
62	5	3844	25	310
73	6	5329	36	438
83	9	6889	81	747
$\sum X = \underline{620}$	$\sum Y = \underline{60}$	$\sum X^2 = \underline{40570}$	$\sum Y^2 = \underline{390}$	$\sum XY = \underline{3951}$

$$r = \frac{10(3951) - (620)(60)}{\sqrt{[10(40570) - (620)^2][10(390) - (60)^2]}}$$

$$= \frac{39510 - 37200}{\sqrt{[405700 - 384400][3900 - 3600]}} = \frac{2310}{\sqrt{6390000}} = \frac{2310}{2528} = 0.91$$

8.4 Calculating the Product Moment Correlation Coefficient, r

Method 2

The second method of calculating r is short and simple, employing deviations from the means of all the X and Y values respectively. The formula is given as:

$$r = \frac{xy}{\sqrt{(\sum x^2)(\sum y^2)}}$$

where r = the product moment correlation coefficient
x = the deviation of any X value from the mean of all the X values
y = the deviation of any Y value from the mean of all the Y values
$\sum$ = the 'sum of'.

Table 23 shows the computation of the correlation between the vocabulary quiz scores and the essay competition marks of ten pupils as in Table 22 above.

Table 23   Calculating the Product Moment Correlation Coefficient (Method 2)

Vocabulary quiz X	Essay competition Y	x	y	x^2	y^2	xy
43	4	− 19	− 2	361	4	38
55	5	− 7	− 1	49	1	7
67	6	+ 5	0	25	0	0
38	4	− 24	− 2	576	4	48
49	5	− 13	− 1	169	1	13
70	7	+ 8	+ 1	64	1	8
80	9	+ 18	+ 3	324	9	54
62	5	0	− 1	0	1	0
73	6	+ 11	0	121	0	0
83	9	+ 21	+ 3	441	9	63
$\sum X = 620$ $M_X = \frac{620}{10} = \underline{62}$	$\sum Y = 60$ $M_Y = \frac{60}{10} = \underline{6}$	$\sum x = 0$	$\sum y = 0$	$\sum x^2 =$ $\underline{2130}$	$\sum y^2 =$ $\underline{30}$	$\sum xy =$ $\underline{231}$

$$r = \frac{\sum xy}{\sqrt{(\sum x^2)(\sum y^2)}} = \frac{231}{\sqrt{(2130)(30)}} = \frac{231}{\sqrt{63900}} = \frac{231}{252.8} = 0.91$$

As a rough and ready guide to the meaning of r, the following table offers a descriptive interpretation.

r	meaning
0.00 to 0.19	a very low correlation
0.20 to 0.39	a low correlation
0.40 to 0.69	a modest correlation
0.70 to 0.89	a high correlation
0.90 to 1.00	a very high correlation

8.5 Rank Order Correlation Coefficients

The product moment correlation coefficient, r, is appropriate in describing the degree of association between two variables when the data are at the interval or the ratio level of measurement.

Very often however, in Education and Physical Education, variables cannot be described with sufficient precision such as to warrant the interval or the ratio level of measurement.

Suppose that instead of scores for the essay competition illustrated in Table 22, page 96, two judges had been required to put the essays in *rank order of merit* from one to ten.

Set out below is the hypothetical rank ordering of Judge A and Judge B in respect of the ten essays. Is there a significant relationship between the two sets of rankings? Spearman's rank order correlation coefficient, r_s, is appropriate in describing the degree of association in the judgements of the two experts.

Spearman's Rank Order Correlation Coefficient (r_s, rho)

Spearman's correlation coefficient (rho) is given by:

$$r_s = 1 - \frac{6 \sum d^2}{n(n-1)(n+1)}$$

where d = the difference in rank between the items in a pair
  n = the number of items
  $\sum$ = 'the sum of'.

Table 24   Rank Ordering of Ten Essays by Two Judges

Essay	Judge No. 1	Judge No. 2	d	d^2
A	10	8	2	4
B	7	9	2	4
C	4	4	0	0
D	1	1	0	0
E	3	5	2	4
F	2	2	0	0
G	9	10	1	1
H	5	6	1	1
J	8	7	1	1
K	6	3	3	9
				$\sum d^2 = 24$

$$r_s = 1 - \frac{6 \sum (d^2)}{n(n - 1)(n + 1)}$$

$$= 1 - \frac{144}{990}$$

$$= 0.855$$

From the rough and ready guide to the meaning of correlation shown on page 98, a value of 0.855 indicates a high correlation between the judgements of the two essay experts. Whether or not that value is *significant* we must leave until the concept of significance is discussed later in the text. In Appendix 6 we test the significance of the results shown in Table 24.

8.6   Kendall's Rank Order Correlation Coefficient (τ, tau)

The Kendall rank order correlation coefficient, τ, is a suitable alternative measure to Spearman's r_s when the data on both measures are at the ordinal level of measurement, or above. For an outline of Kendall's τ, see Siegel (1956, pp. 213–223).

8.7   Some Further Thoughts on Relationships

Let's reconsider for a moment the basic concept of variability that we touched upon in Section 6.7. It will help us grasp the meaning of correlation more fully.

As has already been shown, measures of human variables (height, weight, oxygen uptake, ability, intelligence, etc.) result in a distribution of scores which vary from one to another. The factors known to account for this variability are often numerous, and in many cases, unknown. Whether known or not, they are generally categorized as (a) systematic factors and (b) error factors.

Systematic variability, that is, variability due to systematic factors and *error variability*, that is, variability due to error factors, together constitute TOTAL VARIABILITY.

When 'parcelling up' (the correct term is *partitioning*) variability in this way, the best statistical measure of total variability is the VARIANCE.

The variance is simply the standard deviation squared (S.D.^{2}). Because of its non-linear units of measurement (S.D.^{2}), variance can be thought of as an *amount* of variability, made up of different components.

The *total* variance is made up of *systematic* variance and *error* variance. Kerlinger (1972) describes these components as follows:

'Systematic variance is the variance in measures due to some known or unknown influences that "cause" scores to lean in one direction more than another. Any natural or man-made influences that cause events to happen in a certain predictable way are systematic influences'.

and:

'Error variance is the fluctuation or varying of measures due to chance .... It is the variation in measures due to the usually small and self-compensating fluctuations of measures – now here, now there, now up, now down'.

8.8 The Coefficient of Determination

A correlation coefficient gives a measure of the relationship between two variables. It tells us very little however about the nature of that relationship, only that it exists and that it is either relatively high or low.

A fuller grasp of correlation is gained if we consider the COEFFICIENT OF DETERMINATION. This coefficient ($r^2 \times 100$), determines what percentage of the total variance of variable X is due to the variance of variable Y.

For example:

(a) If the correlation (r) between variable X and variable $Y = 0$, then the coefficient of determination $= 0^2 \times 100 = 0\%$.

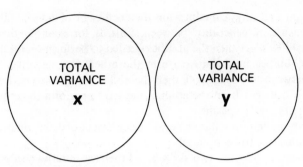

None of the factors accounting for variability are common to both variables.

(*b*) If the correlation (*r*) between variable X and variable $Y = 0.8$, then the coefficient of determination $= 0.8^2 \times 100 = 64\%$.

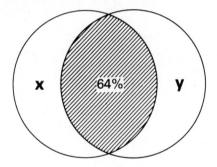

64% of the factors accounting for variability are common to both variables.

(*c*) If the correlation (*r*) between variable X and variable $Y = 1$, then the coefficient of determination $= 1^2 \times 100 = 100\%$.

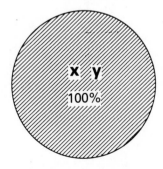

100% of the factors accounting for variability are common to both factors.

In education and physical education the coefficient of determination is often used as a measure of 'generality' between skills. If, for example, the correlation between two skills is + 1 then the abilities needed to perform one skill are identical with the abilities needed to perform the other. On the other hand, if the correlation between two skills is 0, then the abilities needed to perform one skill are completely different from the abilities needed to perform the other, that is to say, the skills are 100% specific.

Notice that one cannot obtain a negative coefficient of determination, since the correlation value has to be squared.

If the correlation between two skills is − 1 then the abilities needed to increase performance in one skill will decrease performance in the other.

Inferential Statistics

9.1 Introduction

Up to this point in the text we have discussed *descriptive statistics*, outlining the central tendencies, the variability, and the relationships in data that are readily at hand. It is time now to move from description to an examination of statistical techniques that enable us to go from *known* to *unknown* data, that is, to make inferences about wider populations from which our 'known' data are drawn. These techniques are called *inferential statistics*. Inferential statistics deal with two different types of problems, the first to do with making estimates, the second, with testing hypotheses. Both tasks involve making inferences about population parameters from sample measures. It is to samples and to sampling methods that we first turn our attention.

We said earlier that it is often impossible to obtain measures of characteristics of a total population. Population characteristics have to be inferred from measures taken from samples. Statistics are taken from samples and, using appropriate inferential techniques, population parameters are estimated.

9.2 Sampling Methods

Regardless of which inferential statistical technique we intend to use, the predictive or inferential power of the test will be governed to a certain extent by the procedure used in selecting the sample. If the sample is not truly representative of the population from which it is drawn, that is, if it is a biased sample, then it becomes virtually impossible to make an accurate prediction about the population.

Bias in sample selection is reduced when methods incorporating at least an element of random selection of subjects are employed. More importantly, the predictions made from such samples have greater validity, because the principles of randomness of selection are fundamental to theories of statistical inference. These theories are based upon the laws of probability and chance.

The methods outlined below all incorporate, in part at least, some random selection of subjects.

9.3 Simple Random Sampling

In simple random sampling, each member of the population under study has an equal chance of being selected. The method involves selecting at random from a list of the population (a sampling frame) the required number of subjects for the sample. Because of probability and chance, the sample should contain subjects with characteristics similar to the population as a whole, i.e. some old, some young, some tall, some short, some fit, some unfit, some rich, some poor, etc. One problem associated with this particular sampling method is that a complete list of the population is needed and this is not always readily available.

9.4 Systematic Sampling

This method is a modified form of simple random sampling. It involves selecting subjects from a population list in a systematic rather than a random fashion. For example, if from a population of say 2,000, a sample of 100 is required, then every 20th person can be selected. The starting point for the selection is chosen at random.

9.5 Stratified Sampling

Stratified sampling involves dividing the population into homogeneous groups, each group containing subjects with similar characteristics. For example, group A might contain males and group B females. In order to obtain a sample representative of the whole population in terms of sex, a random selection of subjects from both group A and B must be taken. If needed, the exact proportion of males to females in the whole population can be reflected in the sample.

9.6 Cluster Sampling

When the population is large and widely dispersed, gathering a simple random sample poses administrative problems. Suppose we want to examine children's fitness levels in a particularly large community? It would be quite impractical to randomly select children and spend an inordinate amount of time travelling about in order to test them. By cluster sampling, we can randomly select a specific number of schools and test all the children in those selected schools.

9.7 Stage Sampling

Stage sampling is an extension of cluster sampling. It involves selecting the sample in stages, that is, taking samples from samples. Using the large community example referred to earlier, one type of stage sampling might be to select a number of schools at random, and from within each of these schools select a number of classes at random, and from within these classes randomly select a number of pupils.

9.8 Sampling Error

If many samples are taken from the same population it is unlikely that they will all have characteristics identical, either to each other or to the population. In a word, there will be *sampling error*.

Sampling error is not necessarily the result of mistakes made in sampling procedures. Rather, variations may occur due to the chance selection of different individuals. For example, if we take a large number of samples from the population and measure the mean value of each sample, then the sample means will not be identical. Some means will be relatively high, some relatively low, and many will cluster around an average or mean value for the samples. Why should this occur?

We can explain this phenomenon by reference to the Central Limit Theorem which is derived from the laws of probability. The Central Limit Theorem states that if random, large samples of equal size are repeatedly drawn from any population, then the means of those samples will be approximately normally distributed. Moreover, the average or mean of the sample means will be approximately the same as the population mean. We can show this diagrammatically as follows:

Figure 40 Distribution of sample means showing the spread of a selection of sample means around the population mean.

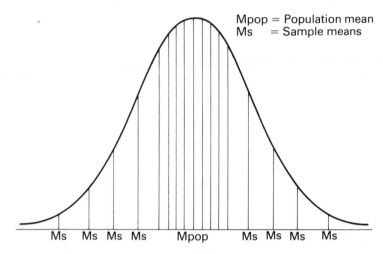

Mpop = Population mean
Ms = Sample means

Ms Ms Ms Ms Mpop Ms Ms Ms Ms

With the Central Limit Theorem in mind, we can see that when a sample is selected and the mean value of a particular characteristic of that sample is calculated, that sample mean is but one of a theoretical distribution of sample means. Moreover, because of sampling error, that particular sample mean is unlikely to be the same as the mean of the population. From our knowledge of the characteristics of a normal distribution however, we know that 68.26% of scores lie between ±1 standard deviations from the mean (i.e. $Z = 1$). It follows then that in the theoretical distribution of sample means, 68.26% of all sample means will lie between ±1 standard deviations from the population mean. Put differently, we know that our particular sample mean has a 68.26% chance of falling between ±1 standard deviations from the population mean.

Furthermore, from Figure 42 we can see that our sample mean has a 95% chance of lying between ±1.96 standard deviations from the population mean (i.e. $Z = ±1.96$); a 99% chance of lying between ±2.58 standard deviations from the population mean (i.e. $Z = ±2.58$), and a 99.73% chance of lying between ±3 standard deviations from the population mean (i.e. $Z = ±3$).

Figure 41 Percentage of sample means ± 1 standard deviation from population mean.

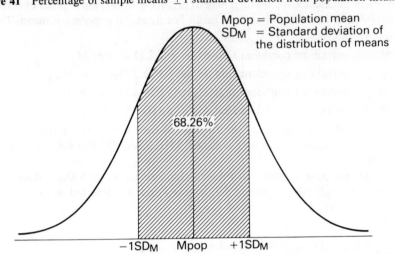

Mpop = Population mean
SD$_M$ = Standard deviation of
the distribution of means

68.26%

−1SD$_M$ Mpop   +1SD$_M$

Figure 42 Further percentages of sample means by standard deviations from population mean.

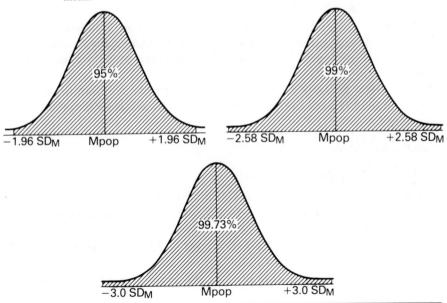

95%

−1.96 SD$_M$ Mpop   +1.96 SD$_M$

99%

−2.58 SD$_M$ Mpop   +2.58 SD$_M$

99.73%

−3.0 SD$_M$ Mpop   +3.0 SD$_M$

Clearly, if we can calculate the standard deviation of the theoretical distribution of sample means, we are then able to predict with varying degrees of certainty or confidence, how far our sample mean lies from the population mean. That is to say we can be:

68.26% certain or confident that M_s is ± 1 S.D.$_M$ from M_{pop}.

95% certain or confident that M_s is ± 1.96 S.D.$_M$ from M_{pop}.

99% certain or confident that M_s is ± 2.58 S.D.$_M$ from M_{pop}.

99.73% certain or confident that M_s is ± 3.00 S.D.$_M$ from M_{pop}.

The standard deviation of the theoretical distribution of sample means is a measure of sampling error and is called THE STANDARD ERROR OF THE MEAN.

So far, we have referred to this standard deviation as S.D.$_M$. More usually however, it is given the symbols S.E.$_M$ or σ_M and is calculated as follows:

$$S.E._M = \frac{S.D._s}{\sqrt{N}}$$

where S.D.$_s$ = the standard deviation of the sample

N = the number in the sample.

Strictly speaking, the formula for the standard error of the mean is:

$$S.E._M = \frac{S.D._{pop}}{\sqrt{N}}$$

where S.D.$_{pop}$ is the standard deviation of the population. However, as we are usually unable to ascertain the S.D. of the whole population, the standard deviation of the sample is used instead. We can illustrate this with a worked example.

Example How far away do we expect the true population mean to lie from a sample mean of 75 when the standard deviation of the sample is 18 and the size of the sample is 36?

$$S.E._M = \frac{S.D._s}{\sqrt{N}} = \frac{18}{\sqrt{36}} = 3$$

Therefore, the population mean has:

a 68.26% chance of lying 75 ± 3, $(M_s \pm 1 \text{ S.E.}_M)$, or between 72 and 78

a 95% chance of lying $75 \pm 1.96 \times 3$, $(M_s \pm 1.96 \text{ S.E.}_M)$, or between 69.12 and 80.88

a 99% chance of lying $75 \pm 2.58 \times 3$, $(M_s \pm 2.58 \text{ S.E.}_M)$, or between 67.26 and 82.74

a 99.73% chance of lying $75 \pm 3.00 \times 3$, $(M_s \pm 3.00 \text{ S.E.}_M)$, or between 66 and 84.

It must be remembered that the mean of the population is a fixed value and does not vary. What the above confidence statements are saying is that the mean of the population is at a fixed but unknown point within a certain interval.

Look at the last confidence statement. Using the interval 66–84, we can conclude that there is only a 0.27% chance $(100\% - 99.73\%)$ that the population mean is at a distance greater than 9, $(3 \times \text{S.E.}_M)$ from the sample mean. Similar conclusions can be made about the other confidence statements.

9.9 Levels of Confidence

The varying degrees of certainty or confidence to which we have referred (68.26%, 95%, 99%, 99.73%) are called the *levels of confidence*. As we now know from the preceding sections, these levels tell us the probability of a sample mean being a certain distance from the population mean. Up to this point in our discussion we have described the levels of confidence in terms of percentages. It's more usual however to state confidence levels as probabilities, as the table of selected confidence levels shows below.

Table 25 Summary of Selected Confidence Levels

Level	Interval range	Probability of sample mean lying within interval (P_B)	Probability of sample mean lying *outside* interval (P_A)
99.73%	$M_{\text{pop}} \pm 3.00 \text{ S.E.}_M$	0.9973	0.0027
99%	$M_{\text{pop}} \pm 2.58 \text{ S.E.}_M$	0.99	0.01
95%	$M_{\text{pop}} \pm 1.96 \text{ S.E.}_M$	0.95	0.05
68.26%	$M_{\text{pop}} \pm 1.00 \text{ S.E.}_M$	0.6826	0.3174

The information in the summary Table 25 can be represented diagrammatically as follows:

Figure 43   Diagrammatic representation of selected confidence levels.

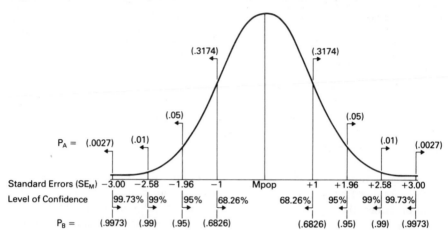

When we define a confidence level in terms of probability we normally use the P_A value. In Figure 43 above, the P_A value is shown above the horizontal axis of the normal curve. The P_A value states the probability of a sample mean lying *outside* the confidence interval. For example, the 0.05 confidence interval is the one *outside* of which a sample mean has only a 5 in 100 chance of lying.

Let's return to the problem of whether a sample mean can be considered to be a representative or reliable estimate of the true population mean.

From our discussion we can now see that the further away a sample mean is from the population mean, the less trust we can place in it. For example, suppose the sample mean lies outside the 0.01 interval. What exactly does this tell us about it? It says, in effect, that it only has a 1 in 100 chance of being representative of the population mean. Put differently, that particular sample mean has a 99 in 100 chance of being non-representative.

9.10 *t* Distributions

In our outline of confidence intervals and limits, we used Table 19 to estimate, for example, that the 0.05 level of confidence is situated at ± 1.96 standard deviations or standard errors from the mean of the population (i.e. $Z = 1.96$). To find the exact limits in actual scores for a particular sample mean we multiplied the calculated S.E.$_M$ by 1.96.

Table 19 can only be used, of course, when the distribution of sample means is normal. If the distribution is not normal then the 0.05 level will not be located at a Z score of ± 1.96. As samples become smaller, their distributions become flatter and more spread out as we show in Figure 44 below. These non-normal distributions are called *t* distributions.

Figure 44 *t* distributions and normal distribution.

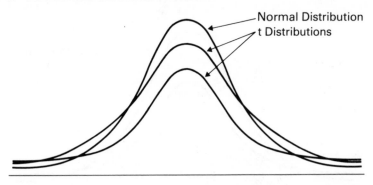

Notice that there is a different *t* distribution for each size of sample.

To obtain a confidence level for a *t* distribution within which 95% of the theoretical sample means lie (i.e. the 0.05 level) we have to move further out in standard deviation units from the mean. We show this diagrammatically in Figure 45 below.

Figure 45   95% confidence level in *t* and normal distributions.

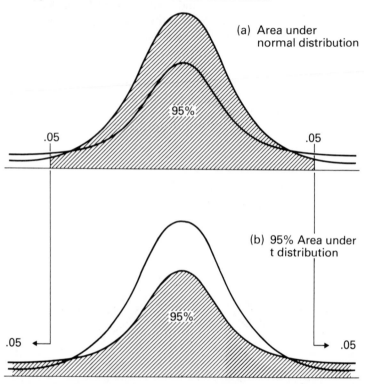

(a) Area under normal distribution

95%

.05   .05

(b) 95% Area under t distribution

95%

.05   .05

In a normal distribution, the distance between the mean and successive points, measured in standard deviation units, is expressed as a *Z* value and this value is used to estimate the area between a particular point and the mean (see Table 19).

In a *t* distribution however, the distance between the mean and successive points, measured in standard deviation units, is expressed as a *t* value. For a given sample size this *t* value can be used to estimate the area between a particular point and the mean. A different table must be consulted however. An abridged *t* distribution table is shown below. It gives the *t* value needed to achieve particular levels of confidence.

Table 26*   An Abridged _t_ Distribution Table

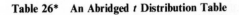

Degrees of Freedom	$P = 0.05$	$P = 0.01$
1	$t = 12.706$	$t = 63.657$
2	$t = 4.303$	$t = 9.925$
5	$t = 2.571$	$t = 4.032$
8	$t = 2.306$	$t = 3.355$
10	$t = 2.228$	$t = 3.169$
14	$t = 2.145$	$t = 2.977$
16	$t = 2.120$	$t = 2.921$
20	$t = 2.086$	$t = 2.845$
30	$t = 2.042$	$t = 2.750$
60	$t = 2.000$	$t = 2.660$
120	$t = 1.980$	$t = 2.617$
∞	$t = 1.960$	$t = 2.576$

*   A comprehensive _t_ table for use at later stages in the text is presented in Appendix 3.

Look at Table 26 above. The _t_ values are shown for the 0.05 and the 0.01 levels of confidence. Notice that they are not set as _t_ values against _N_, but as _t_ values against _degrees of freedom_.

In estimating the population mean from a sample mean the degrees of freedom available are $N - 1$ where $N =$ the number of observations. For example, if we want to establish the 0.05 and the 0.01 levels of confidence for the mean of a population when the sample size is 15, we enter the table at degrees of freedom 14, since d.f. $= N - 1 = 15 - 1 = 14$. The appropriate _t_ values are 2.145 and 2.977 for the 0.05 and the 0.01 levels respectively. We conclude that when sample sizes are 15, 95% of the sample means will lie between ± 2.145 (2.15) standard deviations from the population mean. Moreover, 99% of the sample means will lie between ± 2.977 (2.98) standard deviations from the population mean.

Figure 46 t value at the 95% level of confidence.

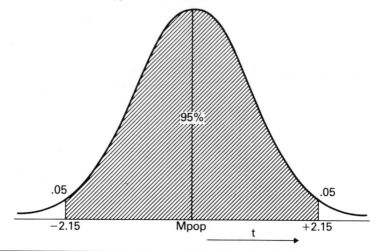

Figure 47 t value at the 99% level of confidence.

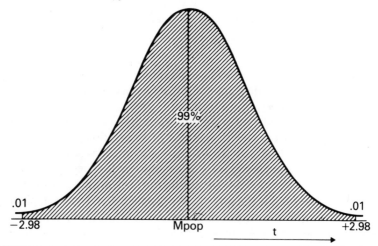

Recall that the standard deviation of a distribution of means $(S.D._M)$ is equal to the standard error of the mean $(S.E._M)$. We can see that once the standard error has been determined, the exact confidence limits, measured in actual scores, can be estimated.

Take for example, sample size 15,

0.05 (95%) confidence interval $= M_s \pm (2.15 \times \text{S.E.}_M)$

0.01 (99%) confidence interval $= M_s \pm (2.98 \times \text{S.E.}_M)$

Let's see how this works out with an actual problem. For a sample size 17, determine the 0.05 (95%) and the 0.01 (99%) confidence intervals for the M_{pop} when the sample mean (M_s) is 50 and the sample standard deviation (S.D.$_s$) is 10.

Step 1 Calculate the standard error of the mean (S.E.$_M$)

For small samples $\text{S.E.}_M = \dfrac{\text{S.D.}_s}{\sqrt{N}} = \dfrac{10}{\sqrt{17}} = \dfrac{10}{4.12} = 2.42$

Step 2 Enter Table 26 for 16 d.f. $(N - 1)$ and find t values for the 0.05 and the 0.01 levels

t for $0.05 = 2.120$, (2.12)

t for $0.01 = 2.921$, (2.92)

Step 3 Establish the confidence limits using:

$M_s \pm t \times \text{S.E.}_M$

For the 0.05 level, $50 \pm (2.12 \times 2.42) = 50 \pm 5.13 = 44.87$ to 55.13

For the 0.01 level, $50 \pm (2.92 \times 2.42) = 50 \pm 7.07 = 42.93$ to 57.07

We conclude that the population mean has a 95% chance of lying at a fixed value somewhere between 44.87 and 55.13. Furthermore, it has a 99% chance of lying between 42.93 and 57.07.

9.11   Degrees of Freedom

Having introduced *degrees of freedom* (d.f.) in the previous section, it's appropriate at this point to deal more fully with this rather difficult concept.

Degrees of freedom is involved in many of the inferential statistical techniques we cover in later sections of the text.

In sampling statistics, the degrees of freedom can loosely be considered equal to the number of observations or scores minus the number of parameters that are being estimated. Thus, in using N sample observations to estimate the mean of the population (the mean being one parameter), the degrees of freedom will be $N - 1$.

The rationale behind this is that if observations or numbers are used to estimate a score about which we can draw a conclusion, then the establishment of that score causes the original observations or numbers to lose a certain amount of freedom.

Look at it this way. Suppose we have to select any five numbers. We have complete freedom of choice as to what the numbers are. So, we have 5 degrees of freedom. Suppose however we are then told that the five numbers must have a total value of 25. We will have complete freedom of choice to select four of the numbers but the fifth will be dependent on the other four. Let's say that the first four numbers we select are 7, 8, 9, and 10 which total 34, then if the total value of the five numbers is to be 25, the fifth number must be -9.

$$7 + 8 + 9 + 10 - 9 = 25$$

A restriction has been placed on one of the observations; only four are free to vary; the fifth has lost its freedom. In our example then d.f. $= 4$, that is, $N - 1 = 5 - 1 = 4$.

Suppose now we are told to select any five numbers, the first two of which have to total 9 and the total value of all five has to be 25.

One restriction is apparent when we wish the total of the first two numbers to be 9. Another restriction is apparent in the requirement that all five numbers must total 25. In other words we have lost two degrees of freedom in our example. It leaves us with d.f. $= 3$, that is, $N - 2 = 5 - 2 = 3$.

Notice that the degrees of freedom available are not always $N - 1$. They depend upon the particular estimation at hand. In each of the inferential statistical techniques outlined later in the text, we set out the specific method for obtaining the appropriate degrees of freedom.

9.12 Hypothesis Formulation and Testing

Hypotheses are hunches that the researcher has about the existence of relationships between variables. Testing hypotheses is to do with accepting or rejecting explanations of those relationships within known degrees of certainty.

This way of looking at hypothesis formulation and testing may seem somewhat strange to the reader. 'Isn't hypothesis testing', the reader might ask, 'concerned with finding *differences* rather than *relationships*'?

The apparent contradiction can be explained by the following example:

... 'suppose a researcher tests the hypothesis that boys will out-perform girls on certain tests of geometrical aptitude. He might divide his sample into a group of boys and a group of girls, administer a geometry aptitude test and see if the two groups perform differently on the test. Now although it may appear that he is looking for a difference between the groups, deeper consideration will reveal that the researcher is really attempting to see if there is a *relationship* between the *variable of sex*, on the one hand, and the *variable of geometry aptitude* on the other. Ultimately, almost all hypotheses in educational research are suppositions about relationships between variables'.

(Popham and Sirotnik, 1973, p. 46)

Nevertheless, as Popham and Sirotnik advise, it is useful for the student researcher to think of the various methods he comes across in inferential statistics in terms of whether they are essentially *difference-testing* or *relationship-testing* techniques.

We deal first with the concept of statistical significance before looking at the formulation and testing of a hypothesis.

Suppose that in the example above, the mean score on a geometric aptitude test in a group of 11 boys is 14 with a standard deviation of 3, and in a group of 11 girls, the mean score is 10 with a standard deviation of 2. The researcher wishes to know whether or not the observed difference in the means of the two groups is *significant*. What exactly is meant by *significant*?*

9.13   Statistical Significance

Recall that in previous sections, we showed that by marking off standard units of distance along the base line of the normal curve, we were able to determine the percentage of a population under specific parts of that curve. The standard scores used to mark off standard units of distance we remember, are called Z scores.

A Z score of 1.96 taken at each end of the normal curve cuts off 5% of the total area of the curve as we illustrate in Figure 48. Similarly, a Z score of 2.58 taken at each end of the normal curve cuts off 1% of the total area of the curve as shown in Figure 49.

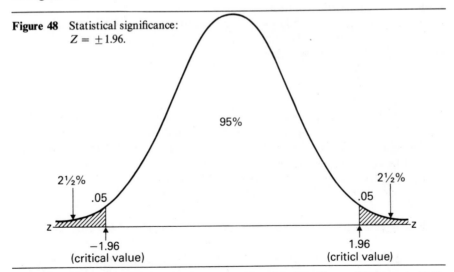

Figure 48 Statistical significance:
$Z = \pm 1.96$.

95%

2½%
.05
z
−1.96
(critical value)

2½%
.05
z
1.96
(criticl value)

---

* We are solely concerned here with the concept of *statistical* significance. What may be highly significant *statistically* may be of no *educational* significance whatsoever!

117

Figure 49 Statistical significance: $Z = \pm 2.58$.

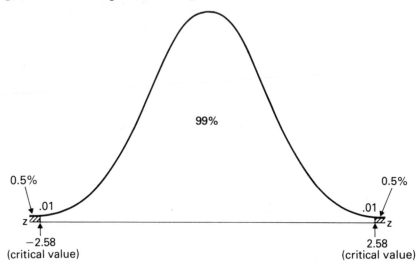

Much of the research undertaken in Education and Physical Education uses what is called the *hypothetico-deductive method*. This involves the statistical testing of a formulated hypothesis.

As stated earlier, a hypothesis is simply a 'hunch', or a statement about an expected relationship, or difference between variables or groups. In our geometrical aptitude example we hypothesize that:

there is a difference between the means of the boys' and the girls' groups.

In order to find out whether there is a statistically significant difference between the two groups, or whether the difference is caused by sampling error, we first have to state our hypothesis in the form of a NULL HYPOTHESIS, generally denoted by the shorthand (H_0).

A null hypothesis (H_0) is *a hypothesis of no difference*. In our example, the null hypothesis would be stated as follows:

there is *no* difference between the means of the boys' and the girls' groups.

The reason why we have to state our hypothesis in the null form is that inferential statistical techniques are designed to allow us to estimate how far above or below zero a difference or relationship can be expected to lie due to random sampling error. The further a difference or relationship is above or below zero, the less chance it has of occurring as a result of random sampling error and the greater chance it has of being statistically significant.

Statistical tests tell us of the probability of a difference or a relationship occurring as a result of chance sampling errors. In Education and Physical Education, we generally accept that if a difference only has a 5 in 100 ($p = 0.05$) chance of being due to sampling error, or 95 in 100 ($p = 0.95$) chance of *not* being due to sampling error, then we take it to be significantly different and we reject H_0, the null hypothesis.

Certain statistical tests give us values in the form of Z scores, the chance probability of which we can determine along the baseline of the normal curve. Thus, from a Z score of 1.96 or more, we can infer that the chance probability of the value occurring is 5 times in 100, written as the probability (p) is less than ($<$) 0.05

that is, $p < 0.05$

Similarly, from a Z score of 2.58 or more, we infer

$p < 0.01$

Other statistical tests give us values in the form of t scores, the chance probability of which we can, again, determine by reference to the base line of a curve which like the normal curve, is symmetrical and has a mean of zero. The shapes of t distributions alter with the size of samples as shown in Figure 44 (page 111). As a general rule of thumb however, when a sample size is greater than 30 ($n > 30$), the t distribution and the Z distribution are taken to be approximately equal.

In our example of differences in geometrical aptitude, if a t value exceeds 2.09 then we can infer that only 5 times in 100 is the difference between the means likely to occur by chance. Put another way, 95 times out of 100, a difference of that size is *statistically significant*. It's not appropriate here to show the detailed computation of t in respect of the mean scores of the two groups in our example (see Section 10.5 for t test calculations). The computed value however is 3.67. Figure 50 shows that 3.67 lies outside of the critical value of 2.09 obtained from Table 26 which indicates $p < 0.05$.

We conclude that there *is* a significant difference between the boys and the girls in their geometrical aptitude and that we must *reject* the null hypothesis.

Figure 50 Diagrammed example: Testing the null hypothesis (two-tailed test).

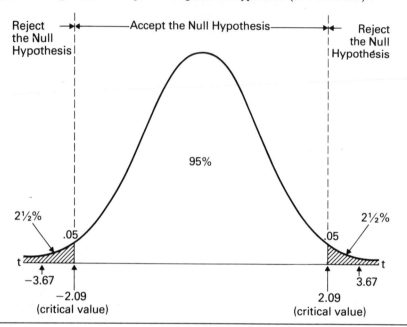

9.14 One-Tailed and Two-Tailed Tests

Notice that in formulating the null hypothesis in our example above we simply stated that there would be no difference between the mean scores on geometrical aptitude. The test of the null hypothesis that we employed was a *non-directional* test; non-directional because we did not specify the direction in which we believed the means would differ. In Figure 50 we established a critical value of 2.09 on either side of the curve, thus allowing for the possibility that our statistical test would give us either a positive or a negative *t* value. Because a non-directional test locates critical values at both 'tails' of the distribution, it is referred to as a *two-tailed* test.

Suppose, however, that prior to giving the test of geometrical aptitude we have good reasons to predict that the boys' mean performance will be significantly superior to that of the girls. Here we are predicting the *direction* in which we expect the difference to lie and we are, in consequence, concerned with only one 'tail' of the distribution. In this event a *one-tailed* test is appropriate. Figure 51 shows the critical value (1.73) of *t* in respect of our sample of 22 boys and girls.

Figure 51   Diagrammed example: Testing the null hypothesis (one-tailed test).

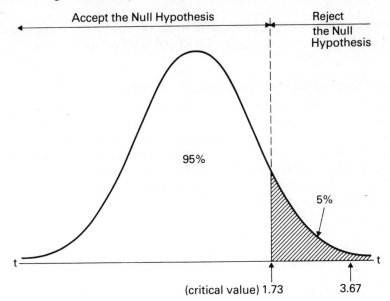

9.15   Type 1 and Type 2 Errors

As we said earlier, it's common practice in Education and Physical Education studies for the researcher to 'accept the 0.05 level of significance' or to 'accept the 0.01 level of significance' in his investigation.

What exactly does this mean?

'Accepting the 0.05 level of significance' in rejecting the null hypothesis means that 95 times out of a 100 we are probably correct in our decision, *but*, 5 times out of 100, we run the risk of rejecting the null hypothesis when in fact it is *true*.

When the null hypothesis is rejected and it is actually true, we refer to a *TYPE 1* error having been committed. How can the risk of committing a Type 1 error be reduced? Simply by setting our level of acceptance at a more rigorous standard, for example, at the 1 in a 1000 times level of significance ($p < 0.001$), or by increasing the sample size.

The reader will appreciate however that the researcher faces a 'swings and roundabouts' situation. The opposite of the case we have just outlined is referred to as a TYPE 2 error, that is, *not* rejecting the null hypothesis when, in fact, it should be rejected.

Thus, as we decrease the possibility of making a TYPE 1 error, we increase the probability of making a TYPE 2.

Most Education and Physical Education researchers are by nature cautious characters. They aim to limit the probability of committing Type 1 errors.

9.16   Independent and Dependent Variables

Recall that in Section 9.12 we gave an example to do with geometric skills among boys and girls and proposed that formulating a hypothesis involved making a supposition about the relationship between *sex* on the one hand, and *geometric aptitude* on the other. We went on to say that almost all educational hypotheses have to do with hunches about relationships between variables.

What sort of relationship might we propose about *sex* and *aptitude for geometry*? That sex is, perhaps, one of a number of variables that are *presumed to cause** geometrical aptitude? The other way round is clearly absurd – that geometrical aptitude is *presumed to cause* sex!

A fundamental way of classifying variables in Education and Physical Education is to do with their *presumed causal* relationships.

An independent variable is the presumed cause of a *dependent* variable. What we are saying in effect is:

If A, then B

In educational and physical educational research, we attempt to predict *from* independent variables *to* dependent variables. Thus:

the sex of the child (independent variable) is the presumed cause of geometrical aptitude (dependent variable),
and,
coaching technique A (independent variable) is the presumed cause of skill rating B (dependent variable).

A variable can, of course, serve both as an independent and as a dependent variable. For example, a researcher may wish to examine the presumed causes of *anxiety* (dependent variable) from among the following independent variables – amount of time in revision, clarity of written instructions, and the difficulty of the questions. On the other hand, his research might feature *anxiety* as an independent variable in a study of the presumed causes of examination failure.

---

* Notice how careful we are to use the phrase 'presumed to cause' rather than 'cause'!

9.17 Correlated and Uncorrelated Data

Recall that in Section 9.3 (page 104) in our discussion of simple random sampling, we said that this method ensures each member of a group an equal chance of being selected. Suppose we draw two samples completely randomly from a population of 1000 pupils. We should rightly expect that the two groups would be unrelated to various characteristics that we might be interested in. Paraphrasing what we said in Section 9.3, pupils in both groups should be both old and young, tall and short, intelligent and dull, swimmers and non-swimmers, and so on. In a word, the data to do with the two groups are unrelated or *uncorrelated*.

Suppose now that we wish to examine the difference between two groups of pupils in respect of *staying on at school after 16+* and that we have matched the groups by *intelligence, social class background* and the *subjects* they are studying. On only one variable are they different, and that is *sex*. Our two groups then, one consisting of boys, the other, girls, have been matched or related in respect of three variables. Our data in this case are *correlated*.

Suppose further that in one of the two groups, say the girls, we are interested in the decision to *stay on at school after 16+* both *prior to* and *immediately after* 'O' level results. Here again, we have an example of correlated data since our two sets of information refer to the same subjects.

Certain statistical techniques, as we shall see, are appropriate in the case of correlated data whilst other techniques are suitable for uncorrelated data.

9.18 Parametric and Non Parametric Statistics: Some Further Observations

In Section 2.4 we were content simply to distinguish between parametric and non parametric methods and to note that unlike parametric techniques which involve assumptions about the distributions of the populations that are sampled, non parametric methods require far fewer assumptions about population data, that is why non parametric tests, as their name implies, may be regarded as 'distribution-free' procedures.

What, then, are the advantages of using non parametric statistics? In the first place, they employ simple formulae! In the second, they are easy and quick to apply and in comparison with parametric tests they can be used under a wide range of conditions. Many of the non parametric tests that we employ in subsequent sections of the text are concerned with the rank ordering, rather than the numerical value of variables or observations. Indeed, as we shall see, sometimes not even rank order is required. In brief, non parametric procedures can be used when data are at the nominal and the ordinal level of measurement.

What are the disadvantages of non parametric tests? Perhaps the most important is to do with what is termed the *power* of a test. The power of a test refers to the probability of rejecting the null hypothesis when, in fact, it is false. The greater the ability of a test to reject a false hypothesis, the greater its relative power.

Power = $1 - \beta$

where β is the probability of a Type 2 error.

Although, in general, non parametric tests are not as powerful as parametric tests, for large samples, they are often more *robust*. This means that often inferences based on non parametric tests are valid, despite the strict assumptions of the equivalent parametric test not being adhered to.

As you will see later in the text, many parametric tests have non parametric equivalents. In order to be more discerning in our selection it is important to have some idea of their relative power. This is done by estimating the *power efficiency* or *asymptotic relative efficiency* (ARE), as it is sometimes called. The power efficiency gives us a single measure of relative performance of two tests, both using large sample sizes. It tells us how much we must increase sample size N in test I (non parametric test) to make it as powerful as test II (parametric test). It is calculated from the following formula:

$$\text{Power efficiency of test I} = (100)\,\frac{N_{II}}{N_{I}}\ \text{per cent}$$

where N_I is the number of cases needed by test I to achieve the same power as test II when it (test II) has N_{II} cases.

For example, if test I needs 30 cases to be as powerful as test II when it has 21 cases, then test I has a power efficiency of $(100)\frac{21}{30} = 70\%$. This indicates that the power of test I using 100 cases is the same as that of test II using 70 cases.

As we have said, non parametric tests are generally less powerful than parametric tests, due in part to dealing in rank orders rather than actual numerical values and therefore 'wasting' a certain amount of available information. However, if the assumptions of a particular parametric test are not met then it is often more appropriate to use an equivalent non parametric test. The advantage here is that since the non parametric test is not based upon parametric assumptions it does not lose its validity when those assumptions are not met. Indeed, it would be more valid than its parametric equivalent, particularly when the sample size is small.

For a more detailed discussion of the merits and limitations of non parametric tests see Gibbons (1976, pages 26–30).

Finally, in Section 10.9 onwards, in which we set out what are termed *Factorial Designs*, readers will grasp an important advantage of parametric over non parametric techniques. When the researcher is interested in interaction effects between variables, it is parametric techniques, such as two way analysis of variance, which permit the assessment of interaction far more readily than non parametric methods.

Choosing an Appropriate Test

EXPERIMENTAL DESIGN		TYPE OF TEST	NATURE OF DATA
Section	One group		
10.1 10.2 10.3 10.4 10.5	Single observations on one variable One observation on each of two variables Repeated observations on same subjects Before/After (time series) Multi-treatment	Parametric	Correlated
		Non parametric	Correlated
			Uncorrelated
Section	TWO GROUP		
10.6 10.7	Static comparison on one variable Before and after treatment		Correlated
		Parametric	Uncorrelated
		Non parametric	Correlated
			Uncorrelated
Section	MULTI GROUP		
10.8	More than two groups, one single variable	Parametric	
		Non parametric	Uncorrelated
Section	FACTORIAL		

10.9
10.10
 	
10.11
	The effect of two independent variables
	The effect of two independent variables
	  (Repeated measures on ONE factor)
	The effect of two independent variables
	  (Repeated measures on BOTH factors)
		Parametric	Correlated

			Uncorrelated

	LEVELS OF MEASUREMENT	
Nominal	**Ordinal**	**Interval/Ratio**
		Pearson product moment corr. coefficient, p 138 t-test for correlated means p 144 One way analysis of variance for correlated means p 161
Cochran Q test p 169, 171 McNemar test p 148, 153	Spearman rank order corr. p 140 Wilcoxon matched pairs test p 146 Sign test p 156 Friedman two way ANOVA p 166	
Chi square one sample test p 131 Kolmogorov Smirnov one sample test p 133 (Ranked categories)		
		t-test for correlated means p 191
		t-test for independent samples p 175 (pooled variance) t-test for independent samples p 178 (separate variance)
	Wilcoxon matched pairs test p 194	
Kolmogorov Smirnov two sample test p 184 Chi square test (2 × k) p 187	Mann-Whitney U test p 179	
		One way analysis of variance p 201 (Single observations of separate groups)
	Kruskal-Wallis one way analysis of variance by ranks, p 212	
		Two way analysis of variance (Repeated measures on ONE factor) p 224 Two way analysis of variance (Repeated measures on BOTH factors) p 233
		Two way analysis of variance p 216

Choosing an Appropriate Test

In the second part of Statistics for Education and Physical Education, we present a number of research designs and illustrate their use with examples drawn from Education and Physical Education.

A standard format is employed throughout.

First, we give a tabular presentation of the research design. Then a concrete example of the design using Education or Physical Education data. Finally the example is worked through, using an appropriate statistical test and illustrating each step of the computation in full.

10.1 One Group Design: Single Observations on One Variable

A. Ordinal, Interval or Ratio Scores

Group 1	Observations$_{(X)}$
Subjects A	X_A
B	X_B
C	X_C
D	X_D

or

B. Nominal Data

	Number of Subjects in Each Category			
	Category 1	Category 2	Category 3	Category k
Group 1. Subjects A, B, C, ..., N				
Observed frequency	$X_{1(0)}$	$X_{2(0)}$	$X_{3(0)}$	$X_{k(0)}$
Expected frequency	$X_{1(e)}$	$X_{2(e)}$	$X_{3(e)}$	$X_{k(e)}$

Example 1   Using the Chi Square (One Sample Test)

Table 27 shows the results of 128 races run over 400 metres, on standard eight-lane tracks, stated in terms of the number of wins by athletes using specific lanes. We wish to know whether the lane in which an athlete is placed in a 400 metres race is likely to affect his chances of winning.

The null hypothesis (H_0) in this case is that the lane in which an athlete is placed in a 400 metres race does not affect his chances of winning.

Table 27   Results of 400 Metre Races

	Lane 1	Lane 2	Lane 3	Lane 4	Lane 5	Lane 6	Lane 7	Lane 8
Observed frequency of wins (O)	18	17	14	15	16	18	17	13

Chi square (χ^2) is probably the most used of all non parametric tests. It is applicable when data are nominal and grouped into categories or boxes. It allows us to test the difference between observed scores and expected or theoretical scores.

PROCEDURES IN COMPUTING CHI SQUARE

1   Estimate the expected frequency (E) for each lane based upon the null hypothesis.

The null hypothesis states that the choice of lane does not affect the chances of winning. Thus each lane is expected to produce the same number of winners, namely 16 (number of races divided by number of lanes).

2   Tabulate the expected frequencies (E) and the observed frequencies (O) as shown below.

Table 28 Observed and Expected Results of 400 Metre Races

	Lane 1	Lane 2	Lane 3	Lane 4	Lane 5	Lane 6	Lane 7	Lane 8
Observed frequency of wins (O)	18	17	14	15	18	16	17	13
Expected frequency of wins (E)	16	16	16	16	16	16	16	16

3 Calculate chi square (χ^2)

$$\chi^2 = \sum \frac{(O - E)^2}{E}$$

where O = observed frequency in each category
   E = expected frequency in each category

$$\chi^2 = \left(\frac{18 - 16}{16}\right)^2 + \left(\frac{17 - 16}{16}\right)^2 + \left(\frac{14 - 16}{16}\right)^2 + \left(\frac{15 - 16}{16}\right)^2 + \left(\frac{18 - 16}{16}\right)^2$$

$$+ \left(\frac{16 - 16}{16}\right)^2 + \left(\frac{17 - 16}{16}\right)^2 + \left(\frac{13 - 16}{16}\right)^2$$

$$= \frac{24}{16} = 1.5$$

4 Determine the degrees of freedom (d.f.). For a one sample chi square test, degrees of freedom are given by the formula $k - 1$, where k equals the number of categories or cells.

   d.f. $= k - 1 = 8 - 1 = 7$

5 Consult the table in Appendix 2 for 7 degrees of freedom. Our value of 1.5 is less than the value in the table at the 0.05 level of confidence (14.07) indicating that there is no significant difference between the observed and expected frequencies. We therefore accept the null hypothesis and conclude that the lane in which an athlete is placed in a 400 metres race does not affect his chances of winning.

YATES CORRECTION

If the number of categories or cells in a chi square analysis is only two, giving just one degree of freedom, the chi square value is subject to error unless an adjustment is made to the formula. This adjustment is known as Yates correction for continuity. It involves subtracting 0.5 from the numerator of each category or cell value of χ^2 as shown in the formula:

$$\chi^2 = \sum \left(\frac{|O - E| - 0.5}{E} \right)^2$$

Garrett (1970) suggests that failure to use the correction causes the probability of a given result to be greatly underestimated and the chances of its being significant considerably increased.

As a general rule, the chi square test is restricted to the use of randomly selected samples of an adequate size. The stability of the test is decreased* if there are less than 5 expected frequencies in any one category or cell. One way around the problem of low expected frequencies is to combine categories or cells, reducing the total number of cells, but increasing the frequencies within those remaining.

The power efficiency of a χ^2 test is not usually reported due to the fact that it is used when no suitable parametric test is available for the same data.

Example 2   Using the Kolmogorov Smirnov One Sample Test

As part of an Educational Research Methods course, students are given the choice of one of four options in computer studies, the options themselves differing only in the time taken to cover a fixed amount of actual material. We wish to find out whether or not student choice of a particular option is related to the period of time over which that option is scheduled.

The null hypothesis (H_0) in this case is that students' option choice is not related to the duration of the option. Table 29 below sets out the choices of 20 students.

Table 29   Student Choice of Educational Research Methods Options

Number of students choosing	Option 1 (6 weeks)	Option 2 (5 weeks)	Option 3 (4 weeks)	Option 4 (3 weeks)
	0	3	8	9

* But see Everitt (1977), page 40, for an alternative view.

Statistics for Education and Physical Education

The Kolmogorov Smirnov One Sample Test, a simple goodness of fit test, is appropriate to the analysis of student choice. It enables us to test the degree of agreement between the distribution of an observed set of values with a specified theoretical distribution.

The assumption governing the use of the Kolmogorov Smirnov One Sample Test is that the underlying dimension is continuous and that the data are at the nominal level of measurement.

The formula employed in the Kolmogorov Smirnov One Sample Test is

$$D = |(CPo - CPe)| \max$$

where D = an obtained result which is compared with STA-TISTIC D in Table 31 below

CPo = an observed cumulative proportion

CPe = an expected cumulative proportion

and $|(CPo - CPe)| \max$ = the greatest divergence between any two proportions.

PROCEDURES IN COMPUTING THE KOLMOGOROV SMIRNOV D STATISTIC

The procedures for calculating D are simple and straightforward.

1 The observed frequencies are converted into cumulative frequencies which are then divided by N to obtain cumulative proportions (CPo).

2 A theoretical cumulative proportion (CPe) is also calculated on the basis that under the null hypothesis, each of the options in the Educational Research Methods course would receive similar choices.

3 The observed cumulative proportion (CPo) is then compared with the theoretical cumulative proportion (CPe) to identify $|CPo - CPe|$ (maximum), that is, the greatest divergence between any two proportions.

4 $|CPo - CPe|$ (max) $= D$, which is then compared with STATISTIC D in Table 31 below to find out whether the obtained D value is statistically significant.

Let's see how D is computed in our example.

Table 30 **Student Choice of Educational Research Methods Options Observed and Expected Cumulative Proportions**

	Option 1 (6 weeks)	Option 2 (5 weeks)	Option 3 (4 weeks)	Option 4 (3 weeks)
No. of students choosing	0	3	8	9
CPo	0/20	3/20	11/20	20/20
CPe	5/20	10/20	15/20	20/20
$(CPo - CPe)$ max	5/20	7/20	4/20	0/20

$$D = 7/20 = 0.35$$

Reference to Table 31 shows that for $N = 20$, the obtained D value of 0.35 exceeds STATISTIC $D = 0.29$ $(p < 0.05)$

and also exceeds STATISTIC $D = 0.33$ $(p < 0.02)$

We therefore reject the null hypothesis and conclude that student choice of a particular option is significantly related to the length of time over which that option is scheduled.

The power efficiency of the Kolmogorov Smirnov one sample test is generally regarded greater than the χ^2 test, as individual observations are treated separately and very small samples can be used.

Table 31   Critical Values of D in the Kolmogorov Smirnov One Sample Test

Sample size N	Significance level	
	0.05	0.02
1	0.975	0.99
2	0.84	0.90
3	0.71	0.78
4	0.62	0.69
5	0.56	0.63
6	0.52	0.58
7	0.48	0.54
8	0.45	0.51
9	0.43	0.48
10	0.41	0.46
11	0.39	0.44
12	0.38	0.42
13	0.36	0.40
14	0.35	0.39
15	0.34	0.38
16	0.33	0.37
17	0.32	0.36
18	0.31	0.35
19	0.30	0.34
20	0.29	0.33
21	0.29	0.32
22	0.28	0.31
23	0.27	0.31
24	0.27	0.30
25	0.26	0.30
26	0.26	0.29
27	0.25	0.28
28	0.25	0.28
29	0.24	0.27
30	0.24	0.27

Source: Adapted from Table 4.4, Ray Meddis, *Statistical Handbook for Non-Statisticians*, London: McGraw-Hill, 1975, p. 63, with the kind permission of the author and publisher.

10.2 One Group – One Observation per Subject on Each of Two Variables

Group 1	Observations on Variable 1 (X)	Observations on Variable 2 (Y)
Subjects A	X X_A	Y Y_A
B	X_B	Y_B
C	X_C	Y_C
D	X_D	Y_D

Example 1 _Using the Pearson Product Moment Correlation_

A sample of 10 students is drawn at random and measured for leg power and leg speed with the following results.

Table 32   Student Leg Power and Leg Speed

Students	Leg power	Leg speed
A	5.2	115.0
B	7.9	129.5
C	5.4	120.0
D	4.4	117.5
E	6.7	115.0
F	3.8	117.0
G	7.1	117.0
H	6.0	111.0
I	4.7	124.5
J	6.6	130.5

We wish to find out whether there is a relationship between leg power and leg speed. The Pearson Product Moment Correlation coefficient is a suitable measure of relationship when samples are randomly selected from normally distributed populations.

The null hypothesis (H_0) in this case is that there is no relationship between leg power and leg speed.

The Pearson Product Moment Correlation Coefficient is given by the formula:

$$r = \frac{N \sum XY - (\sum X)(\sum Y)}{\sqrt{[N \sum X^2 - (\sum X)^2][N \sum Y^2 - (\sum Y)^2]}}$$

where r = product moment correlation
          N = number of pairs of scores
          X = scores on variable X
          Y = scores on variable Y
          $\sum$ = 'sum of'.

PROCEDURES IN COMPUTING THE PEARSON PRODUCT MOMENT CORRELATION COEFFICIENT

1   Total the scores on leg power $(\sum X)$ and the scores on leg speed $(\sum Y)$.

2   Square each student's scores on leg power (X^2) and leg speed (Y^2).

3 Sum the X^2 values giving $\sum X^2$, and sum the Y^2 values giving $\sum Y^2$.

4 Multiply each student's score for leg power (X) by his score on leg speed (Y) to give his XY value.

5 Sum the XY values $(\sum XY)$.

Table 33 Computing the Correlation Between Leg Power and Leg Speed

Student	Leg power (X)	Leg speed (Y)	X^2	Y^2	XY
A	5.2	115.0	27.04	13225.0	598.0
B	7.9	129.5	62.41	16770.25	1023.05
C	5.4	120.0	29.16	14400.0	648.0
D	4.4	117.5	19.36	13806.25	517.0
E	6.7	115.0	44.89	13225.0	770.5
F	3.8	117.0	14.44	13689.0	444.6
G	7.1	117.0	50.41	13689.0	830.7
H	6.0	111.0	36.00	12321.0	666.0
I	4.7	124.5	22.09	15500.25	585.15
J	6.6	130.5	43.56	17030.25	861.30

$\sum X = 57.8$ $\sum Y = 1197.0$ $\sum X^2 =$ 349.36 $\sum Y^2 =$ 143656.0 $\sum XY =$ 6944.3

Substituting our data from Table 33 above,

$$r = \frac{10(6944.3) - (57.8)(1197)}{\sqrt{[10(349.36) - (57.8)^2][10(143656) - (1197)^2]}}$$
$$= 0.33$$

Consult the table in Appendix 5 for significance of correlation when $N = 10$. Our value of 0.33 is less than the value in the table at the 0.05 level $(r = 0.63)$. We therefore accept the null hypothesis and conclude that there is not a significant relationship between leg speed and leg power.

Example 2 Using Spearman's Rank Order Correlation Coefficient

As part of a progress assessment, twelve children in a remedial English group are rated on their attainment on both reading skill and word recognition. Their teacher then puts the children into rank order of achievement on both tests. The data are set out in Table 34 below.

Table 34 Rank Ordering of Attainment on Reading and Word Recognition

Pupil	Variable X (reading skill)	Variable Y (word recognition)
Bill	4	6
Fred	7	9
John	6	5
Jim	12	11
Tom	10	8
Sarah	1	1
George	9	10
Andy	2	2
Jean	11	12
Paul	5	3
Simon	8	7
Alan	3	4

We wish to find out whether there is a significant relationship between reading and word recognition in this small group. The null hypothesis (H_0) in this case is that reading and word recognition are not related.

Spearman's Rank Order Correlation Coefficient (r_s) is appropriate to our task.

The assumptions for using r_s are that the sample is randomly selected and that the data are at the ordinal level of measurement.

Spearman's r_s is given by:

$$r_s = 1 - \frac{6 \sum d^2}{n(n - 1)(n + 1)}$$

where d = the difference in rank between the items in a pair

n = the number of items

$\sum$ = the sum of.

PROCEDURES IN COMPUTING SPEARMAN'S r_s

1 Rank the subjects on variable X from 1 to N, assigning 1 to the highest ranking and so on.

2 Rank the subjects on variable Y from 1 to N, assigning 1 to the highest ranking and so on.

3 Compute d for each subject by subtracting his Y ranking from his X ranking.

4 Compute d^2 for each subject by squaring his d value.

5 Compute $\sum d^2$ by summing all of the d^2 values.

6 Where tied observations occur, each subject is assigned the average of the ranks that would have been given, had no ties occurred. A small number of tied observations has little effect on r_s. Where a large number of tied observations occur, a correction factor is introduced into the computation of r_s (see Siegel, 1956, pp. 206–210 for a fuller discussion).

Table 35   Rank Ordering of Attainment on Reading and Word Recognition: Computation

Pupil	Variable X (reading skill) rank X	Variable Y (word recognition) rank Y	d	d^2
Bill	4	6	-2	4
Fred	7	9	-2	4
John	6	5	1	1
Jim	12	11	1	1
Tom	10	8	2	4
Sarah	1	1	0	0
George	9	10	-1	1
Andy	2	2	0	0
Jean	11	12	-1	1
Paul	5	3	2	4
Simon	8	7	1	1
Alan	3	4	-1	1
				$\sum d^2 = 22$

Statistics for Education and Physical Education

Substitute from Table 35 into the formula:

$$r_s = 1 - \frac{6 \sum d^2}{n(n-1)(n+1)} = 1 - \frac{6 \times 22}{12(11)(13)} = 1 - \frac{132}{1716}$$

$$r_s = 0.924$$

Recalling our rough-and-ready guide to the strength of a correlation coefficient (see page 98) there is a very high relationship between reading skill and word recognition. The significance of the relationship can be tested by reference to the table in Appendix 6.

Interpolating in that table at $n = 12$, we see that an r_s value of 0.506 is necessary for significance of the 5% level and that an r_s value of 0.712 must be reached for significance at the 1% level. Our obtained value exceeds both of these values. We therefore reject the null hypothesis and conclude that there is a significant correlation between the reading skill and word recognition rankings.

With larger samples (where $n = 10$ or more) an alternative way of testing the significance of r_s is suggested by Kendall (1948) employing the t test.

The formula is given by:

$$t = r_s \sqrt{\frac{N-2}{1-r_s^2}}$$

In our example above

$$t = 0.924 \sqrt{\frac{N-2}{1-0.854}}$$

$$= 0.924 \sqrt{68.49} = 7.65$$

Degrees of freedom are determined by d.f. $= n - 2$ where n is the number of ranks being compared. Reference to the table in Appendix 3, shows that for d.f. $= 10$, a t value of 2.23 is significant at the 5% level and a t value of 3.17 is significant at the 1% level. Our obtained value of $t = 7.65$ exceeds both of these values. We therefore reject the null hypothesis and conclude that there is a significant correlation between the rank ordering of our two variables, reading skill and word recognition.

The power efficiency of the Spearman Rank Order Correlation Test relative to the Pearson Product Moment Test is reported to be 91.2% (Gibbons 1976).

10.3 One Group: Repeated Observation on the Same Subjects Under Two Conditions

Group 1	Condition 1	Condition 2
Subjects A	X_{A_1}	X_{A_2}
B	X_{B_1}	X_{B_2}
C	X_{C_1}	X_{C_2}
D	X_{D_1}	X_{D_2}

or

Before and After Treatment

Group 1	Before Treatment Observations (b)	After Treatment Observations (a)
Subjects A	$X_{A_{(b)}}$	$X_{A_{(a)}}$
B	$X_{B_{(b)}}$	$X_{B_{(a)}}$
C	$X_{C_{(b)}}$	$X_{C_{(a)}}$
D	$X_{D_{(b)}}$	$X_{D_{(a)}}$

Example 1   Using t-Test for Correlated Data

Ten Physical Education students are randomly selected to take part in an experiment to determine if reaction time to a visible stimulus is different from reaction time to an audible stimulus.

The null hypothesis (H_0) in this case is that there is no difference between reaction times to visual and auditory stimuli.

Table 36   Reaction Times to Visual and Auditory Stimuli

Subjects	Reaction time to visual stimulus (m. secs)	Reaction time to auditory stimulus (m. secs)
A	289	225
B	278	190
C	255	207
D	246	205
E	288	235
F	304	288
G	223	193
H	223	211
I	317	270
J	285	231

When data are at the interval level of measurement and taken from one randomly selected sample on two occasions, or from two matched samples on one occasion, the difference between the two sets of data can be estimated using the t-test for correlated means.

't' is given by the formula:

$$t = \frac{\sum D}{\sqrt{\dfrac{N \sum D^2 - (\sum D)^2}{N - 1}}}$$

where D is the difference between each subject's two scores and N is the number of subjects.

PROCEDURES IN COMPUTING t FOR CORRELATED DATA

1   Compute the difference (D) between each subject's two scores.

2   Square D's for each subject.

3 Sum the D values algebraically to give $\sum D$.

4 Sum the D^2 values to give $\sum D^2$.

Table 37 Reaction Times to Visual and Auditory Stimuli: Computation Procedures

Subjects	Reaction time to visual stimulus (X_A)	Reaction time to auditory stimulus (X_B)	D $(X_A - X_B)$	D^2 $(X_A - X_B)^2$
A	289	225	64	4096
B	278	190	88	7744
C	255	207	48	2304
D	246	205	41	1681
E	288	235	53	2809
F	304	288	16	256
G	233	193	40	1600
H	223	211	12	144
I	317	270	47	2209
J	285	231	54	2916
			$\sum D = 463$	$\sum D^2 = 25759$

Substituting our data from Table 37 above:

$$t = \frac{463}{\sqrt{\dfrac{10(25759) - (463)^2}{10 - 1}}}$$

$$= 6.68$$

Degrees of freedom are given by the formula:

d.f. $= N - 1 = 9$

Enter the table in Appendix 3 at d.f. $= 9$. If our estimated value is larger than the values in the table then it is significant at those levels of confidence.

Our value of $t = 6.68$ is larger than that shown at the 0.05 level ($t = 2.26$) and that shown at the 0.01 level ($t = 3.25$). We therefore reject the null hypothesis and conclude that there is a significant difference between reaction times to a visible and an audible stimulus.

Statistics for Education and Physical Education

Example 2 Using the Wilcoxon Matched-Pairs Signed Ranks Test

The research department of a major shoe manufacturing company has designed a football boot with a revolutionary new sole which they claim will improve a player's mobility and speed on the field. In order to test this claim 14 players are selected at random and given one pair of traditionally designed boots (Boot A) and one pair of the newly designed boots (Boot B). Each player is then required to complete two timed agility runs on grass, one run wearing Boot A and the other wearing Boot B.

Do the following results indicate that the newly designed boots improve performance on the agility run? The null hypothesis (H_0) in this case is that there is no difference in the agility run performance of the subjects in the two conditions, Boot A and Boot B. Note that in testing the null hypothesis in this particular example, we are asking whether the difference in performance on the agility run will favour Boot B. In other words, our test of the null hypothesis is directional and a one-tailed test is appropriate.

The Wilcoxon Test is designed to test the difference between two related sets of rankable scores, the two observations being made either on the same or matched subjects.

Table 38 Agility Test Performances with Boot A and Boot B

Subject or pairs	Wearing traditional boots (Boot A)	Wearing newly designed boots (Boot B)
	Agility test performance (secs.)	
A	23.8	23.9
B	25.5	24.5
C	25.2	25.3
D	25.5	25.0
E	25.7	25.2
F	24.9	24.4
G	24.6	24.9
H	24.7	24.5
I	23.9	24.2
J	26.4	27.0
K	25.0	25.5
L	25.8	25.3
M	24.3	24.0
N	25.2	24.3

PROCEDURES IN COMPUTING THE WILCOXON MATCHED-PAIRS SIGNED-RANKS TEST

1 For each subject or pair determine the difference in scores (d).

2 Rank these differences ignoring the plus or minus signs and differences of 0. When ranks are tied assign the average of the tied ranks.

3 Assign each rank the $+$ or $-$ sign of the difference it represents.

Table 39   Computation of Agility Test Performance Data

	Boot A	Boot B	d	Rank of d	Rank with less frequent sign
A	23.8	23.9	−0.1	−1.5	1.5
B	25.5	24.5	1.0	14	
C	25.2	25.3	−0.1	−1.5	1.5
D	25.5	25.0	0.5	9	
E	25.7	25.2	0.5	9	
F	24.9	24.4	0.5	9	
G	24.6	24.9	−0.3	−5	5
H	24.7	24.5	0.2	3	
I	23.9	24.2	−0.3	−5	5
J	26.4	27.0	−0.6	−12	12
K	25.0	25.5	−0.5	−9	9
L	25.8	25.3	0.5	9	
M	24.3	24.0	0.3	5	
N	25.2	24.3	0.9	13	
					$T = 34$

4 Note the ranks with the less frequent sign.

5 Total (T) the ranks with the less frequent sign

$T = 1.5 + 1.5 + 5 + 5 + 12 + 9$
$= 34$

6 Consult Table 71 (page 197) for $N = 14$. If the estimated T value is less than that in the table there is a significant difference between the sets of scores at that level.

Our value of $T = 34$ is greater than that in the table for a one-tailed test at the 0.05 level. We therefore accept the null hypothesis and conclude that the newly designed boots do not improve performance on the agility run.

When samples in the Wilcoxon Test are large (> 25) Table 71 (page 197) is not applicable and the T value has to be transformed into a Z score using,

$$Z = \frac{T - \dfrac{N(N + 1)}{4}}{\sqrt{\dfrac{N(N + 1)(2N + 1)}{24}}}$$

The significance of Z can be obtained from Table 72 (page 198).

The power efficiency of the Wilcoxon Matched-Pairs Signed Ranks Test relative to the t-test for correlated means is reported as 95.5% (Gibbons 1976).

Example 3 Using the McNemar Test for the Significance of Change

Very often in Education and Physical Education, when we are interested in the effects of a particular activity upon the performance of our subjects, we are able to organize our data into a *before-and-after* design in which each individual acts as his own control. *For example, listed below are the scores of 32 pupils who were classified on the fluency of their reading before and after a short intensive course intended to improve their reading skills.*

Fluency was judged as follows: absolutely fluent (5), good fluency (4), moderate fluency (3), weak fluency (2), and very poor fluency (1).

Table 40   Reading Fluency Before and After Course

Pupil name	Fluency classification before course	Fluency classification after course
Bill	1	2
Jean	3	4
Joan	4	3
Fred	2	3
Sue	5	5
Sharon	4	4
Andy	3	4
George	1	2
Alan	1	2
Mike	2	3
Jane	4	5
Amanda	5	4
Lesley	4	4
Jenny	4	5
Doreen	5	5
Tom	2	4
Keith	1	2
Adrienne	3	4
Joyce	4	5
Frank	1	2
Philip	2	2
Steven	1	3
Tricia	5	4
Melanie	4	5
Louise	3	4
Margaret	2	4
Peter	1	3
Jeremy	4	5
Michael	1	2
Anna	5	4
Naomi	3	4
Pauline	3	4

Statistics for Education and Physical Education

We wish to know whether what appears to be an overall improvement in the class of pupils' fluency levels is, in fact, a significant change. The null hypothesis (H_0) in this case is that the observed improvement is no different from what could be expected to occur by chance.

The McNemar Test for the Significance of Change is appropriate to our task.

The assumptions for using the McNemar Test are that the pairs of scores on observations are randomly drawn from a population and that the data are either at nominal or ordinal levels of measurement.

The McNemar Test for the Significance of Change is given by the formula:

$$\chi^2 = \frac{(|A - D| - 1)^2}{A + D}$$

where the data have been cast into a fourfold table such as the one below

After

		−	+
	+	A	B
Before			
	−	C	D

and where the − 1 in the formula is a correction factor for continuity (see Siegel, 1956, page 64 for a fuller discussion).

PROCEDURES FOR COMPUTING THE McNEMAR TEST

1   For each pair of scores or observations, record the direction of changes. Sum to obtain the values A and D.

2   If $\frac{1}{2}$ of $A + D$ is less than 5 then the McNemar Test cannot be employed. Use the Binomial Test instead (see Table 44, page 157).

3   Compute χ^2 and determine significance by reference to the table in Appendix 2.

Table 41 Direction of Changes in Reading Fluency

Pupil name	Fluency classification before course	Fluency classification after course	Direction of change
Bill	1	2	+
Jean	3	4	+
Joan	4	3	−
Fred	2	3	+
Sue	5	5	0
Sharon	4	4	0
Andy	3	4	+
George	1	2	+
Alan	1	2	+
Mike	2	3	+
Jane	4	5	+
Amanda	5	4	−
Lesley	4	4	0
Jenny	4	5	+
Doreen	5	5	0
Tom	2	4	+
Keith	1	2	+
Adrienne	3	4	+
Joyce	4	5	+
Frank	1	2	+
Philip	2	2	0
Steven	1	3	+
Tricia	5	4	−
Melanie	4	5	+
Louise	3	4	+
Margaret	2	4	+
Peter	1	3	+
Jeremy	4	5	+
Michael	1	2	+
Anna	5	4	−
Naomi	3	4	+
Pauline	3	4	+

Statistics for Education and Physical Education

Cast the data in Table 41 into a fourfold table such as the one shown below.

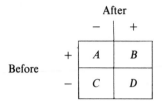

If a pupil's fluency classification remains unchanged, enter his tally either in Box *C* or Box *B*. It does not matter which box is used since we are only interested in Boxes *A* and *D*, that is, those that show where changes have occurred.

Fourfold Classification of Pupils' Fluency Ratings

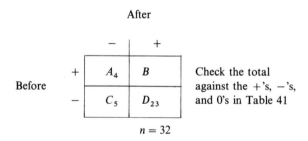

The McNemar Test for the Significance of Change is given by:

$$\chi^2 = \frac{(|A - D| - 1)^2}{A + D}$$

Substituting from the fourfold classification above:

$$\chi^2 = \frac{(|4 - 23| - 1)^2}{27} = 12.0$$

From the table in Appendix 2 we see that at d.f. $= 1$, a value of 3.84 is significant at the 5% level and a value of 6.63 is significant at the 1% level. Our obtained value of 12.0 is in excess of these. We therefore reject the null hypothesis and conclude that the change in fluency ratings for the class of pupils as a whole is significant.

Example 4 Using the McNemar Test for the Significance of Change

A random sample of 50 students who have never participated in rock climbing are asked whether they like or dislike the activity and their responses are noted. They are then taken rock climbing and given instruction. After the period of instruction they are asked the same question and their responses are again noted. The data are shown in the following 2 × 2 contingency table.

Table 42   Attitudes to Rock Climbing

		After instruction	
		Dislike $(-)$	Like $(+)$
Before Instruction	Like $(+)$	*Cell A* 15	*Cell B* 18
	Dislike $(-)$	*Cell C* 13	*Cell D* 4

Cell A   Contains the number of students who like the activity before instruction but dislike it after instruction.

Cell B   Contains the number of students who like the activity both before and after instruction.

Cell C   Contains the number of students who dislike the activity both before and after instruction.

Cell D   Contains the number of students who dislike the activity before instruction and like the activity after instruction.

We can use the McNemar Test to determine whether there is a significant change in attitude towards rock climbing after a period of instruction. The null hypothesis (H_0) in this case is that there is no significant change in attitude as a consequence of the experience of rock climbing.

The assumptions for using the McNemar Test are that the pairs of scores or observations are randomly drawn from a population and that the data are either at nominal or ordinal levels of measurement.

The McNemar Test for the Significance of Change is given by the formula:

$$\chi^2 = \frac{(|A - D| - 1)^2}{A + D}$$

where A = the number of scores or observations in Cell A
and D = the number of scores or observations in Cell D.

PROCEDURES FOR COMPUTING THE McNEMAR TEST

1 Substitute the values in Cell A and Cell D into the formula given above.

2 If $\frac{1}{2}$ of $A + D$ is less than 5 then the McNemar Test cannot be employed. Use the Binomial Test instead. (See Table 44, page 157.)

Substituting from the four fold classification in Table 42 above

$$\chi^2 = \frac{(|15 - 4| - 1)^2}{15 + 4} = \frac{100}{19} = 5.26$$

Degrees of freedom are given by the formula

d.f. = (rows − 1)(columns − 1)
 = (2 − 1)(2 − 1)
 = 1

From the table in Appendix 2 we see that at d.f. = 1, a value of 3.84 is significant at the 5% level of confidence. Our obtained value of 5.26 exceeds this. We therefore reject the null hypothesis and conclude that there is a significant change in attitude towards rock climbing after a period of instruction.

Seigel (1956) reports that when the data are such that a parametric t-test can be applied, the McNemar test has a power efficiency of 95% for $A + D = 6$, declining as $A + D$ increases, to about 63%. Using nominal data, as in example 4, there is no parametric test against which the McNemar test can be compared for power.

10.4 One Group – Before and After (Time Series) Design

Group 1	Before treatment repeated observations (b)	After treatment repeated observations (a)
Subjects A	$X_{A_{(b)}} \, X_{A_{(b)}} \, X_{A_{(b)}} \, X_{A_{(b)}}$	$X_{A_{(a)}} \, X_{A_{(a)}} \, X_{A_{(a)}} \, X_{A_{(a)}}$
B	$X_{B_{(b)}} \, X_{B_{(b)}} \, X_{B_{(b)}} \, X_{B_{(b)}}$	$X_{B_{(a)}} \, X_{B_{(a)}} \, X_{B_{(a)}} \, X_{B_{(a)}}$
C	$X_{C_{(b)}} \, X_{C_{(b)}} \, X_{C_{(b)}} \, X_{C_{(b)}}$	$X_{C_{(a)}} \, X_{C_{(a)}} \, X_{C_{(a)}} \, X_{C_{(a)}}$
D	$X_{D_{(b)}} \, X_{D_{(b)}} \, X_{D_{(b)}} \, X_{D_{(b)}}$	$X_{D_{(a)}} \, X_{D_{(a)}} \, X_{D_{(a)}} \, X_{D_{(a)}}$
E	$X_{E_{(b)}} \, X_{E_{(b)}} \, X_{E_{(b)}} \, X_{E_{(b)}}$	$X_{E_{(a)}} \, X_{E_{(a)}} \, X_{E_{(a)}} \, X_{E_{(a)}}$

Example 1 Using the Sign Test

As part of a Psychology course student teachers are required to take part in an experiment entitled 'Knowledge of Results'.

The experiment aims to find out whether or not knowledge of results aids performance in judging (by sense of touch) the length of a wooden rod.

Briefly, each subject is blindfolded and allowed 50 attempts (in a series of 5 × 10 tries) to estimate the length of a 9 cm. wooden rod and to draw a line of the same length on a piece of paper.

In the 'before' treatment condition subjects are given NO FEEDBACK at all about their 50 attempts to match the length of the wooden rod in their drawings.

In the 'treatment' condition, each time a line is drawn that is within ±5 mm. of the correct length of 9 cm., subjects are informed, 'THAT IS CORRECT'.

In Table 43 below are the results of 16 subjects. We wish to know whether feedback significantly affects performance in the experiment task. The null hypothesis (H_0) in this case is that task performance is not related to feedback.

Table 43   Knowledge of Results Data

Group 1	'Before' treatment NO FEEDBACK No. of correct responses in each of 10 tries					'Treatment' FEEDBACK No. of correct responses in each of 10 tries				
Subject	10	10	10	10	10	10	10	10	10	10
A	0	1	1	2	0	2	4	5	5	6
B	0	0	0	0	0	0	2	1	2	3
C	4	0	4	4	4	5	5	6	7	8
D	0	0	0	0	1	0	0	0	0	0
E	0	1	0	0	0	0	0	0	2	2
F	0	0	0	0	0	0	0	0	0	0
G	0	1	1	2	2	1	3	2	3	4
H	0	0	1	1	1	1	1	2	2	1
I	3	2	0	1	3	4	4	5	6	6
J	0	0	1	0	0	0	0	0	0	0
K	2	0	2	2	3	3	2	4	4	1
L	2	3	2	4	2	4	4	4	6	4
M	1	0	1	1	1	2	0	2	2	1
N	2	1	2	1	1	2	3	3	3	4
O	0	1	1	2	2	0	2	2	1	4
P	0	1	0	1	0	2	2	2	4	2

The Sign Test is appropriate to our problem. The Sign Test makes no assumptions about the form of the distribution of differences between the before treatment and treatment conditions, nor does it require that our subjects are randomly selected or even drawn from the same population. The only assumption made in using the Sign Test is that the variable under investigation has a continuous distribution.

PROCEDURES IN COMPUTING THE SIGN TEST WITH
SMALL SAMPLES ($N < 25$)

1 Record the sign of difference between the scores for each subject as shown in the last column of our example below. (See Table 45, page 158.)

2 Drop from the analysis any subject for whom a difference of 0 is recorded.

3 Count up the number of *fewer* signs. Let these be x.

Table 44 Binomial Test

N \ x	0	1	2	3	4	5	6	7	8	9	10	11	12	13	14	15
5	031	188	500	812	969	†										
6	018	109	344	656	891	984	†									
7	008	062	227	500	773	938	992	†								
8	004	035	145	363	637	855	965	996	†							
9	002	020	090	254	500	746	910	980	998	†						
10	001	011	055	172	377	623	828	945	989	999	†					
11		006	033	113	274	500	726	887	967	994	†	†				
12		003	019	073	194	387	613	806	927	981	997	†	†			
13		002	011	046	133	291	500	709	867	954	989	998	†	†		
14		001	006	029	090	212	395	605	788	910	971	994	999	†	†	
15			004	018	059	151	304	500	696	849	941	982	996	†	†	†
16			002	011	038	105	227	402	598	773	895	962	989	998	†	†
17			001	006	025	072	166	315	500	685	834	928	975	994	999	†
18			001	004	015	048	119	240	407	593	760	881	952	985	996	999
19				002	010	032	084	180	324	500	676	820	916	968	990	998
20				001	006	021	058	132	252	412	588	748	868	942	979	994
21				001	004	013	039	095	192	332	500	668	808	905	961	987
22					002	008	026	067	143	262	416	584	738	857	933	974
23					001	005	017	047	105	202	339	500	661	798	895	953
24					001	003	011	032	076	154	271	419	581	729	846	924
25						002	007	022	054	115	212	345	500	655	788	885

4 Count up the total number of paired observations against which either a + or a − sign has been recorded. Call these N.

5 For $N \leq 25$, enter Table 44 down the left-hand column for N and across the top row for x. At their intersection is the *one-tailed* probability associated with a value as small as x. For a *two-tailed* test multiply p by 2.

Table 45 Computation of Knowledge of Results Data

Group 1	'Before' treatment NO FEEDBACK No. of correct responses in each of 10 tries					T O T A L	'Treatment' FEEDBACK No. of correct responses in each of 10 tries					T O T A L	Sign of difference
Subject	10	10	10	10	10		10	10	10	10	10		
A	0	1	1	2	0	4	2	4	5	5	6	22	+
B	0	0	0	0	0	0	0	2	1	2	3	8	+
C	4	0	4	4	4	16	5	5	6	7	8	31	+
D	0	0	0	0	1	1	0	0	0	0	0	0	−
E	0	1	0	0	0	1	0	0	0	2	2	4	+
F	0	0	0	0	0	0	0	0	0	0	0	0	0
G	0	1	1	2	2	6	1	3	2	3	4	13	+
H	0	0	1	1	1	3	1	1	2	2	1	7	+
I	3	2	0	1	3	9	4	4	5	6	6	25	+
J	0	0	1	0	0	1	0	0	0	0	0	0	−
K	2	0	2	2	3	9	3	2	4	4	1	14	+
L	2	3	2	4	2	13	4	4	4	6	4	22	+
M	1	0	1	1	1	4	2	0	2	2	1	7	+
N	2	1	2	1	1	7	2	3	3	3	4	15	+
O	0	1	1	2	2	6	0	2	2	1	4	9	+
P	0	1	0	1	0	2	2	2	2	4	2	12	+
												$x = 2$ $N = 15$	

From Table 45 above we find that:

$N = 15$ (we drop subject F from the analysis)

and

$x = 2$

Entering Table 44 at $N = 15$ and $x = 2$, the one-tailed probability of our obtained value occurring by chance is 0.004. Since we made no prediction about the direction in which differences in the before treatment and treatment comparisons would occur, we apply a two-tailed test to our findings.

$2 \times 0.004 = 0.008$

We therefore reject the null hypothesis and conclude that since only 8 in 1000 times could our result have occurred by chance, feedback has a significant effect upon the performance of our student teachers.

COMPUTING THE SIGN TEST WITH LARGER SAMPLES $(N > 25)$

For samples where N is greater than 25 use the formula:

$$Z = \frac{(x \pm \frac{1}{2}) - \frac{1}{2}N}{\frac{1}{2}\sqrt{N}}$$

where x and N have the same meaning as before and where $\pm\frac{1}{2}$ is used as a correction factor. When x is less than $\frac{1}{2}N$ (i.e. $x < \frac{1}{2}N$) the correction factor is $+\frac{1}{2}$. When x is greater than $\frac{1}{2}N$ (i.e. $x > \frac{1}{2}N$) the correction factor is $-\frac{1}{2}$.

Let us see how this works out with an example.

Suppose we have the following data:

$N = 100$

$x = 30$

Our correction factor will be $+\frac{1}{2}$ since 30 is less than $\frac{1}{2}N$ (50). Substituting in the formula:

$$Z = \frac{(x + \frac{1}{2}) - \frac{1}{2}N}{\frac{1}{2}\sqrt{N}} = \frac{30.5 - 50}{\frac{1}{2}\sqrt{100}} = \frac{-19.5}{5} = -3.9$$

Reference to Table 72 (page 198) shows that the probability of a $Z = -3.9$ is $2 \times (0.00005) = 0.0001$. (Assuming again that we are applying a two-tailed test.) We would reject the null hypothesis therefore and conclude from these data that our result is significant.

The power efficiency of the Sign Test relative to the t-test is reported as 63.7% for large samples (Gibbons 1976).

10.5 One Group – Multi-Treatment: Treatments as Independent Variable

Group	After treatment 1	After treatment 2	After treatment 3	After treatment 4
Subjects A	X_{A_1}	X_{A_2}	X_{A_3}	X_{A_4}
B	X_{B_1}	X_{B_2}	X_{B_3}	X_{B_4}
C	X_{C_1}	X_{C_2}	X_{C_3}	X_{C_4}
D	X_{D_1}	X_{D_2}	X_{D_3}	X_{D_4}

Example 1 Using One-Way Analysis of Variance-Correlated Means (with Repeated Measures on the Same Subjects or Separate Measures on Matched Subjects)

Analysis of variance techniques are designed to test differences between the means of several (> 2) groups of scores and are based upon the analysis of factors known or unknown which account for the variability of scores.

Recall in Section 8.7 (page 99) we explained how the *total* variability or variance of a set of scores can be divided up or partitioned into *systematic variance* and *error variance*. We said that systematic variance is that part of the total variance caused by factors which lean scores in one direction or the other and that error variance is that part of the total variance caused by chance fluctuations in measures.

Analysis of variance involves the further partitioning and subsequent analysis of those systematic and error variances. As we shall see, the methods of partitioning differ depending upon the particular experimental design that we employ.

Differences between group means are tested by calculating the statistic F which compares the variability between group measures (means) with the variability between individual scores within the group.

Use of analysis of variance demands that the following assumptions be met:
(a) scores are measured on at least an interval scale
(b) samples are taken at random
(c) samples are taken from normally distributed populations
(d) the variances of the sample populations are equal.

Example The haemoglobin levels in the blood of a randomly selected group of physical education students are measured on three separate occasions over a period of six months giving the following results.

Table 46 **Haemoglobin Levels Over a Period of Time**

Subjects	\multicolumn{3}{c}{Haemoglobin level}		
	Oct. (X_1)	Feb. (X_2)	May (X_3)
A	16.4	15.6	15.3
B	15.2	15.3	13.7
C	15.0	15.3	15.3
D	16.7	16.5	16.2
E	16.7	15.5	15.2
F	16.7	14.5	14.6
G	14.5	14.9	14.6
H	15.0	16.2	16.2

Statistics for Education and Physical Education

We wish to determine whether haemoglobin levels change significantly over the given time period. The null hypothesis in this case is that there is no change in haemoglobin levels over the given time period.

The *total* variance in this repeated measures design can be partitioned into:

SYSTEMATIC EFFECTS

1 BETWEEN TRIALS VARIANCE is the variance between group means caused by the independent variable, that is, the period of time between testing.

2 BETWEEN SUBJECT VARIANCE is the variance due to the same subjects being measured on three occasions, thus giving correlated data. Some subjects, for example, score consistently higher than others on all three occasions.

ERROR EFFECTS

3 INTERACTION or RESIDUAL VARIANCE is caused by individual variations on the three different testing occasions. It measures factors due not only to the individual effects of subjects, or time of testing, but to the *joint* effect of these variables; hence the term *interaction*.

$$F_{\text{BETWEEN TRIALS}} = \frac{\text{Between trials variance}}{\text{Interaction or residual variance}}$$

$$F_{\text{BETWEEN SUBJECTS}} = \frac{\text{Between subjects variance}}{\text{Interaction or residual variance}}$$

$$\text{where Variance} = \frac{\text{Sum of squares}}{\text{Degrees of freedom}}$$

PROCEDURES FOR COMPUTING ONE-WAY ANALYSIS OF VARIANCE (CORRELATED MEANS)

1 Square all the scores and include in Table 47.

2 Sum all the raw scores $(\sum X)$ and calculate the grand total (GT).

$$GT = \frac{(\sum X)^2}{N} = \frac{(\sum X_1 + \sum X_2 + \sum X_3)^2}{N}$$

where N = Total number of scores (24)

$$GT = \frac{(371.1)^2}{24} = \frac{137715.21}{24}$$

$$= 5738.13$$

3 Compute the TOTAL sum of squares (SS_{TOTAL}).

$$SS_{TOTAL} = \sum X^2 - GT$$

where $\sum X^2 = \sum X_1^2 + \sum X_2^2 + \sum X_3^2$
$$= 5753.77 - 5738.13$$
$$= 15.64$$

4 Compute the BETWEEN TRIALS sum of squares (SS_{TRIALS}).

$$SS_{TRIALS} = \frac{(\sum X_1)^2 + (\sum X_2)^2 + (\sum X_3)^2}{N_s} - GT$$

where N_s = Number of subjects

$$= \frac{(126.2)^2 + (123.8)^2 + (121.10)^2}{8} - 5738.13$$

$$= 5739.76 - 5738.13$$

$$= 1.63$$

Table 47   Haemoglobin Levels Over a Period of Time: Computational Procedures

Subjects	Oct. X_1	X_1^2	Feb. X_2	X_2^2	May X_3	X_3^2	Totals $(X_1 X_2 + X_3)$
A	16.4	268.76	15.6	243.36	15.3	234.09	47.3
B	15.2	231.04	15.3	234.09	13.7	187.69	44.2
C	15.0	225	15.3	234.09	15.3	234.09	45.6
D	16.7	278.89	16.5	272.25	16.2	262.44	49.4
E	16.7	278.89	15.5	240.25	15.2	231.04	47.4
F	16.7	278.89	14.5	210.25	14.6	213.16	45.8
G	14.5	210.25	14.9	222.01	14.6	213.16	44
H	15.0	225	16.2	262.44	16.2	262.44	47.4

$\sum X_1 = 126.2$ $\sum X_2 = 123.8$ $\sum X_3 = 121.10$ $\sum X = 371.1$
$\sum X_1^2 = 1996.92$ $\sum X_2^2 = 1918.74$ $\sum X_3^2 = 1838.11$ $\sum X^2 = 5753.77$

---

5 Compute the BETWEEN SUBJECTS sum of squares.

$$SS_{\text{SUBJECTS}} = \frac{(X_A)^2}{N_T} + \frac{(X_B)^2}{N_T} + \cdots + \frac{(X_H)^2}{N_T} - GT$$

where X_A = Subject A's total scores on all occasions

N_T = Number of trials

$$= \frac{(47.3)^2}{3} + \frac{(44.2)^2}{3} + \frac{(45.6)^2}{3} + \frac{(49.4)^2}{3} + \frac{(47.4)^2}{3}$$

$$+ \frac{(45.8)^2}{3} + \frac{(44)^2}{3} + \frac{(47.4)^2}{3} - 5738.13$$

$$= 5745.92 - 5738.13$$

$$= 7.80$$

6 Compute INTERACTION or RESIDUAL sum of squares (SS_{INT}).

$$SS_{\text{INT}} = SS_{\text{TOTAL}} - (SS_{\text{SUBJECTS}} + SS_{\text{TRIALS}})$$

$$= 15.64 - (7.80 + 1.63)$$

$$= 6.21$$

7 Compute the degrees of freedom for each sum of squares

d.f. for $SS_{\text{TOTAL}} = (N - 1) = (24 - 1) = 23$

where N = number of scores

d.f. for $SS_{\text{TRIALS}} = (k - 1) = (3 - 1) = 2$

where k = number of trials or columns

d.f. for $SS_{\text{SUBJECTS}} = (r - 1) = (8 - 1) - 7$

where r = number of rows or subjects

d.f. for $SS_{\text{INT}} = (r - 1)(k - 1) = (8 - 1)(3 - 1) = 14$

8 Estimate the variances

$$\text{Variance} = \frac{\text{Sum of squares}}{\text{d.f.}}$$

$$\text{Var.}_{\text{TRIALS}} = \frac{SS_{\text{TRIALS}}}{\text{d.f.}_{\text{TRIALS}}} = \frac{1.63}{2} = 0.81$$

$$\text{Var.}_{\text{SUBJECTS}} = \frac{SS_{\text{SUBJECTS}}}{\text{d.f.}_{\text{SUBJECTS}}} = \frac{7.80}{7} = 1.11$$

$$\text{Var.}_{\text{INT}} = \frac{SS_{\text{INT}}}{\text{d.f.}_{\text{INT}}} = \frac{6.21}{14} = 0.44$$

9 Compute F values for between trials and between subjects

$$F_{\text{TRIALS}} = \frac{\text{Var.}_{\text{TRIALS}}}{\text{Var.}_{\text{INT}}} = \frac{0.81}{0.44} = 1.84$$

$$F_{\text{SUBJECTS}} = \frac{\text{Var.}_{\text{SUBJECTS}}}{\text{Var.}_{\text{INT}}} = \frac{1.11}{0.44} = 2.52$$

10 Enter results in an Analysis of Variance table.

Table 48 Analysis of Variance Table

Source of variation	Sum of squares	d.f.	Variance (mean square)	F
Between trials	1.63	2	1.63/2 = 0.81	1.84
Between subjects	7.80	7	7.8/7 = 1.11	2.52
Interaction	6.21	14	6.21/14 = 0.44	
Total	15.64	23		

11 Refer to the table in Appendix 4 to determine the significance of each F value. Our F value for trials (1.84) is less than the value in the table (3.74) for d.f.$_{\text{TRIALS}} = 2$ and d.f.$_{\text{INT}} = 14$ at the 0.05 level. We therefore accept the null hypothesis and conclude that there is no significant difference in haemoglobin levels over the specified six month period.

Our F value for subjects (2.52) is less than the value in the table (2.78) for d.f.$_{\text{SUB}} = 7$ and d.f.$_{\text{INT}} = 14$ at the 0.05 level. We therefore accept the null hypothesis and conclude that there is no significant difference between subjects when considering them without regarding trials.

Example 2   Using the Friedman Two-Way Analysis of Variance

Having been shown an outline of their first year Education studies, eight student teachers are asked to rank order their preferences for three textbooks in Educational Psychology, all of which are readily available for close inspection. We wish to find out whether or not there is a significant bias towards one particular textbook. The data in connection with students' choice are set out below. The null hypothesis (H_0) in this case is that student choice is not directed towards any one particular psychological text.

Table 49   Students' Choice of Textbooks

Subjects	Textbook choice		
	Book 1	Book 2	Book 3
A	2	1	3
B	2	1	3
C	3	2	1
D	2	1	3
E	3	2	1
F	3	2	1
G	2	1	3
H	3	1	2

What we are asking is simply, do the overall rankings of the three texts differ significantly?

The Friedman Two-Way Analysis of Variance is appropriate to our problem. In our example we are looking at the same group of subjects (the eight student teachers) under each of three conditions (their choices of three textbooks).

The Friedman test assumes ordinal level data.

The formula for its computation looks a little difficult but is really quite straightforward.

$$\chi_r^2 = \frac{12H}{NK(K + 1)} - 3N(K + 1)$$

where $N =$ the number of rows
   $K =$ the number of columns
and $R^2 =$ the square of the rank total
and $H =$ the sum of the squares of the rank totals, i.e. $\sum R^2$.

Let us see how this works out with our data on textbook choice.

Table 50   Students' Choice of Textbooks: Calculation of χ_r^2

	Textbook choice		
Subjects	Book 1	Book 2	Book 3
A	2	1	3
B	2	1	3
C	3	2	1
D	2	1	3
E	3	1	2
F	3	2	1
G	2	1	3
H	3	1	2
	$R_1 = 20$	$R_2 = 10$	$R_3 = 18$

PROCEDURES FOR COMPUTING χ_r^2 (THE FRIEDMAN TEST)

1 Calculate the necessary elements for the formula. Thus:

$N = 8$

$K = 3$

$(R_1)^2 = 400; \qquad (R_2)^2 = 100; \qquad (R_3)^2 = 324$

$H = (R_1)^2 + (R_2)^2 + (R_3)^2 = 824$

2 Substitute in the formula:

$$\chi_r^2 = \frac{12H}{NK(K+1)} - 3N(K+1) = \frac{12(824)}{(8)(3)(3+1)} - 24(3+1)$$

$$= 103 - 96 = 7.00$$

We may test the significance of our findings by entering Table 51 (below) at the appropriate column (that is where $N = 8$ and $K = 3$).

We see that a value $\chi_r^2 = 7.00$ is significant at $p = 0.05$. We therefore reject the null hypothesis and conclude that there is a significant bias in students' choice of an educational psychology text in favour of Book 2.

The power efficiency of the Friedman Test relative to the parametric F test for correlated means is reported as $95.50(k)/(k+1)\%$ where k is the number of columns.

Table 51 Critical Values of χ_R^2 in the Friedman Two Way Analysis of Variance

k = 3			k = 3			k = 3			k = 4			k = 5		
n	0.05	0.01	n	0.05	0.01	n	0.05	0.01	n	0.05	0.01	n	0.05	0.01
2	—	—	21	6.095	9.238	40	6.050	9.150	4	7.800	9.600	2	7.600	8.000
3	6.000	—	22	6.091	9.091	41	6.195	9.366	5	7.800	·9.960	3	8.533	10.23
4	6.500	8.000	23	6.348	9.391	42	6.143	9.190	6	7.600	10.20	4	8.800	11.20
5	6.400	8.400	24	6.250	9.250	43	6.186	9.256	7	7.800	10.54	5	8.960	11.68
6	7.000	9.000	25	6.080	8.960	44	6.318	9.136	8	7.650	10.50	6	9.067	11.87
7	7.143	8.857	26	6.077	9.308	45	6.178	9.244	9	7.667	10.73	7	9.143	12.11
8	6.250	9.000	27	6.000	9.407	46	6.043	9.435	10	7.680	10.68	8	9.200	12.30
9	6.222	9.556	28	6.500	9.214	47	6.128	9.319	11	7.691	10.75	9	9.244	12.44
10	6.200	9.600	29	6.276	9.172	48	6.167	9.125	12	7.700	10.80			
11	6.545	9.455	30	6.200	9.267	49	6.041	9.184	13	7.800	10.85			
12	6.500	9.500	31	6.000	9.290	50	6.040	9.160	14	7.714	10.89		k = 6	
13	6.615	9.385	32	6.063	9.250				15	7.720	10.92			
14	6.143	9.143	33	6.061	9.152				16	7.800	10.95	n	0.05	0.01
15	6.400	8.933	34	6.059	9.176		k = 4		17	7.800	11.05			
16	6.500	9.375	35	6.171	9.314				18	7.733	10.93	2	9.357	9.929
17	6.118	9.294	36	6.167	9.389	n	0.05	0.01	19	7.863	11.02	3	9.857	11.76
18	6.333	9.000	37	6.054	9.243				20	7.800	11.10	4	10.39	12.82
19	6.421	9.579	38	6.158	9.053	2	6.000	—	21	7.800	11.06			
20	6.300	9.300	39	6.000	9.282	3	7.400	9.000	22	7.800	11.07			

Source: Table 4.3. Neave, H. R.; *Statistics Tables*, London: George Allen & Unwin, 1978, p. 49, with the kind permission of the author and publisher.

Example 3   Using the Cochran Q Test

Four trained coaches devise systems for predicting the outcome of tennis matches. In order to test whether each coach is equally effective in his ability to predict outcomes, ten matches are selected at random and the coaches asked to predict the outcome of each match.

The results of correct (1) or incorrect (0) predictions are noted.

Table 52   Tennis Coaches' Predictions of Match Outcomes

| | Coach | | | | Totals | |
Match	A	B	C	D	R	R^2
1	1	0	1	1	3	9
2	1	1	1	0	3	9
3	1	1	1	1	4	16
4	1	0	0	1	2	4
5	0	1	0	1	2	4
6	1	1	0	1	3	9
7	1	0	1	1	3	9
8	0	1	1	1	3	9
9	0	1	1	1	3	9
10	0	1	1	1	3	9
Totals C	6	7	7	9	$T = 29$	$\sum R^2 = 87$
C^2	36	49	49	81	$\sum C^2 = 215$	

Using the Cochran Q Test we can find out if there is a significant difference between prediction methods. The null hypothesis (H_0) in this case is that there is no difference between the tennis coaches' predictions of match outcomes.

Cochran's Q is given by the formula:

$$Q = \frac{(k - 1)(k \sum C^2 - T^2)}{kT - \sum R^2}$$

where $k =$ the number of groups
   $R =$ the total of the rows
   $C =$ the total of the columns
   $T =$ the grand total.

169

PROCEDURES FOR COMPUTING COCHRAN'S Q TEST

1 Compute the row totals (R).

2 Square the row totals (R^2).

3 Compute the column totals (C).

4 Square the column totals (C^2).

5 Sum the row totals $(\sum R) = 29$.

6 Sum the column totals $(\sum C) = 29$.

7 Sum the squares of row totals $(\sum R^2) = 87$.

8 Sum the square of column totals $(\sum C^2) = 215$.

Substituting our data from Table 52 above,

$$Q = \frac{(4 - 1)(4(215) - (29)^2)}{(4)(29) - 87}$$

$$Q = \frac{57}{29} = 1.96$$

We refer to the table for χ^2 (Appendix 2) since Q approximates χ^2 when the numbers of rows are not too small.

Degrees of freedom are given by the formula:

d.f. $= k - 1 = 4 - 1 = 3$

We see that for d.f. $= 3$ a value of Q or $\chi^2 = 7.81$ must be obtained to be significant at the 0.05 level of confidence.

We therefore accept the null hypothesis and conclude that there is no significant difference between the coaches' prediction methods.

Example 4   Using Cochran's Q Test

Postgraduate Certificate of Education students about to begin a compulsory Physical Education course in Biomechanics were asked to say YES or NO as to whether they felt that their studies in Biomechanics would be useful to them in their future work as P.E. teachers. Tutors teaching the course believed they had detected considerably greater enthusiasm for the forthcoming work among those P.G.C.E. students with some 'science background' in their original degree studies. Moreover, a pre-course quiz on general science knowledge had revealed such a wide disparity of understanding that staff also concluded that pre-course knowledge of science might also affect student judgements. Accordingly, they divided the 150 or so P.G.C.E. students into 10 sets on the results of their scores on the general science quiz. They then selected one student from each set in each of the broad areas into which they had been categorized on the subjects of their original degree studies.

Below are recorded the responses of these students to the question, 'Do you think the Biomechanics course will assist you in your future work as a Physical Education teacher?'

Table 53   Yes (1) or No (0) Responses of Students

Student sets	Maths/ Science group	Sociology/ Psychology group	Biology/ Zoology group	English/ History group	Modern languages group
1	1	0	1	0	0
2	1	1	1	0	0
3	0	0	1	0	0
4	1	1	1	0	0
5	1	0	0	1	1
6	1	1	1	0	0
7	1	0	1	0	0
8	1	0	1	1	0
9	1	1	1	0	0
10	1	1	1	1	0

We wish to know whether or not there is evidence that students' original degree studies influenced their responses to the question. The null hypothesis (H_0) in this case is that degree study area is not related to students' responses.

Cochran's Q Test is appropriate to our problem. It provides us with a method of testing whether, with dichotomous data at the nominal level of measurement

Statistics for Education and Physical Education

such as our YES/NO answers, the responses of N sets of subjects under the K conditions of their original degree studies are significantly different from one another.

We are asking, simply, do the K conditions have a significant effect upon the students' responses to our question?

Cochran's Q is given by the formula:

$$Q = \frac{(k-1)(k \sum C^2 - T^2)}{kT - \sum R^2}$$

where X = the scores, in our example Yes = 1, No = 0
k = the number of groups
n = the number of sets of scores or subjects
R = the total of the rows
C = the total of the columns
T = the grand total.

PROCEDURES FOR COMPUTING COCHRAN'S Q

1 Cast the data in the form of a table such as the one illustrating our example below.

Table 54   Student Responses to the Question Concerning Biomechanics

Student sets	'Treatment 1' Maths/ Science group	'Treatment 2' Sociology/ Psychology group	'Treatment 3' Biology/ Zoology group	'Treatment 4' English/ History group	'Treatment 5' Modern Languages group	R
1	1	0	1	0	0	2
2	1	1	1	0	0	3
3	0	0	1	0	0	1
4	1	1	1	0	0	3
5	1	0	0	1	1	3
6	1	1	1	0	0	3
7	1	0	1	0	0	2
8	1	0	1	1	0	3
9	1	1	1	0	0	3
10	1	1	1	1	0	4
$C =$	9	5	9	3	1	$T = 27$

2 Calculate the necessary elements for the formula. Thus:

k = the number of groups = 5

$\sum C^2 = 81 + 25 + 81 + 9 + 1 = 197$

$\sum R^2 = 4 + 9 + 1 + 9 + 9 + 9 + 4 + 9 + 9 + 16 = 79$

$T^2 = 729$

3 Substituting in the formula:

$$Q = \frac{(k-1)(k \sum C^2 - T^2)}{kT - \sum R^2} = \frac{4(5 \times 197 - 729)}{5 \times 27 - 79} = \frac{1024}{56} = 18.28$$

4 Because Q approximates to the chi square distribution if the number of rows (that is, the size of n) is not too small, we can test the significance of Q by reference to the Chi Square Table in Appendix 2.

First we must determine the number of degrees of freedom; d.f. is given by $k - 1$. In our example, $k - 1 = 4$.

Entering the table at d.f. = 4, we see that a Q value of 13.28 is significant at $p = 0.01$. Our value exceeds this. In rejecting the null hypothesis we may conclude that with respect to our original question concerning the Biomechanics course, there is a significant difference in students' responses on the basis of their groupings according to their original degree studies.

As there is no equivalent parametric test with which to compare the Cochran Q test, no measure of power efficiency is reported.

10.6 Two Group Research Designs: Static Comparison on One Variable

Group 1	Subjects A, B, C, D	Group 2	Subjects E, F, G, H
X_1	X_a	X_2	X_e
	X_b		X_f
	X_c		X_g
	X_d		X_h

Example 1   Using the 't' Test for Independent Samples (Pooled Variance)

Do the following scores indicate that Physical Education students have a lower resting heart rate than non-Physical Education students? Our null hypothesis (H_0) in this case is that there is no significant difference between the two groups. Notice that in testing the null hypothesis here, we are looking at the direction in which an expected difference between Physical Education and non-Physical Education students might lie. Thus, a one-tailed test is appropriate.

Table 55   Resting Heart Rates of P.E. and Non-P.E. Students

P.E. students	Non-P.E. students
Resting heart rate (X_1)	Resting heart rate (X_2)
68	79
71	78
58	73
61	75
62	73
65	71
52	70
67	67
63	72
70	68

The t test allows us to determine whether or not the means of the two samples differ so much that the samples are unlikely to have been drawn from the same population. The parametric t test is the one most commonly used by student researchers who wish to test the significance of the difference between the means of two independent samples.

There are various formulae for t depending upon the particular circumstances governing the data. In this first example of the use of t, the following assumptions are made:

(i)   that the groups are independent and have been randomly sampled.
(ii)   that the population variances are equal.
(iii)   that the population distributions are normal.

Statistics for Education and Physical Education

The formula for t is given as:

$$t = \frac{\dfrac{\sum X_1}{N_1} - \dfrac{\sum X_2}{N_2}}{\sqrt{\left(\dfrac{\sum X_1^2 - [(\sum X_1)^2/N_1] + \sum X_2^2 - [(\sum X_2)^2/N_2]}{N_1 + N_2 - 2}\right)\left(\dfrac{N_1 + N_2}{N_1 N_2}\right)}}$$

where $\sum X_1$ = sum of scores, group 1
$\sum X_2$ = sum of scores, group 2
$\sum X_1^2$ = sum of squares, group 1
$\sum X_2^2$ = sum of squares, group 2
N_1 = numbers in group 1
N_2 = numbers in group 2

PROCEDURES FOR COMPUTING t (POOLED VARIANCE)

1 Square the individual scores in both groups.

2 Sum the scores $(\sum X)$ and the squares of scores $(\sum X^2)$ for each group.

Table 56 Computing P.E. and Non-P.E. Student Scores

P.E. students		Non-P.E. students	
X_1	X_1^2	X_2	X_2^2
68	4624.	79	6241.
71	5041.	78	6084.
58	3364.	73	5329.
61	3721.	75	5625.
62	3844.	73	5329.
65	4225.	71	5041.
52	2704.	70	4900.
67	4489.	67	4489.
63	3969.	72	5184.
70	4900.	68	4624.
$\sum X_1 = 637$	$\sum X_1^2 = 40881.$	$\sum X_2 = 726$	$\sum X_2^2 = 52846.$

Substituting our data from Table 56 above:

$$t = \frac{\dfrac{637}{10} - \dfrac{726}{10}}{\sqrt{\left(\dfrac{40881 - [(637)^2/10] + 52846 - [(726)^2/10]}{10 + 10 - 2}\right)\left(\dfrac{10 + 10}{(10)(10)}\right)}}$$

$$= \frac{-8.9}{\sqrt{4.9}}$$

$$= -4.02$$

Degrees of freedom is given by the formula:

d.f. $= N_1 + N_2 - 2$

d.f. $= 10 + 10 - 2 = 18$

(Enter the table in Appendix 3 at 18 d.f. for a one-tailed test.)

Our value of 4.02 (ignore minus sign) is larger than the values in the t table for the 0.05 level ($t = 1.73$) and the 0.01 level ($t = 2.55$). We therefore reject the null hypothesis and conclude that physical education students do have significantly lower resting heart rates than non-physical education students.

The formula used in our example above is called the pooled variance formula. When dealing with large groups of unequal standard deviations it is more applicable to employ the separate variance formula:

$$t = \frac{M_1 - M_2}{\sqrt{\dfrac{SD_1^2}{N_1} + \dfrac{SD_2^2}{N_2}}}$$

where $M_1 =$ mean of sample 1
   $M_2 =$ mean of sample 2
   $SD_1 =$ standard deviation of sample 1
   $SD_2 =$ standard deviation of sample 2
   $N_1 =$ numbers in sample 1
   $N_2 =$ numbers in sample 2.

In consulting the table in Appendix 3 for the significance of t found by the separate variance formula, the t value that our estimated value is compared with is an *average* value, if sample sizes are unequal.

For example, if we calculated a t value of 2.4, using groups of 10 and 15 respectively, and we wanted to determine if that value was significant at the 0.05 level, we would first have to look into the table for 9 d.f. ($N_1 - 1 = 10 - 1$, group 1) and find the t at the 0.05 level ($t = 2.26$). We would then consult the table for 14 d.f. ($N_2 - 1 = 15 - 1$, group 2) and find the t at the 0.05 level ($t = 2.15$).

The t value that our value is compared with is the *average of the two values.*

$$\text{Average } t \text{ at } 0.05 \text{ level} = \frac{2.26 + 2.15}{2}$$

$$= 2.21$$

We therefore conclude that our value of 2.4 is significant at the 0.05 level, being larger than the average t value (2.21) in the table.

For a more detailed discussion about the use of pooled or separate variance formulae, see *Popham and Sirotnik*, pages 139–142.

Example 2   Using the t Test for Independent Samples (Separate Variance)

The mean scores and standard deviations of two groups consisting of 72 boys and 65 girls on an Arithmetic test are set out in Table 57 below. We wish to find out whether the mean scores differ significantly. The null hypothesis (H_0) in this case is that boys' and girls' arithmetic scores are no different from one another.

Table 57   Arithmetic Test Scores of Boys and Girls

	Boys	Girls
	$N_1 = 72$	$N_2 = 65$
	$M_1 = 19.6$	$M_2 = 15.4$
	$SD_1 = 3.2$	$SD_2 = 4.7$

The t test allows us to determine whether or not the means of the two samples differ so much that the samples are unlikely to have been drawn from the same population.

There are various formulae for t depending upon the particular circumstances governing the data. In the example above the following assumptions are made:
(i)   that the groups are independent and have been randomly sampled,
(ii) that the population variances are unequal or heterogeneous, and
(iii) that the population distributions are normal.

PROCEDURES FOR COMPUTING t

The formula for computing t is:

$$t = \frac{M_1 - M_2}{\sqrt{\dfrac{SD_1^2}{N_1} + \dfrac{SD_2^2}{N_2}}}$$

1 Substitute in the formula

$$t = \frac{19.6 - 15.4}{\sqrt{\dfrac{(3.2)^2}{72} + \dfrac{(4.7)^2}{65}}} = \frac{4.2}{0.69} = 6.09$$

Before we can test the significance of our t value of 6.09 obtained by the separate variance formula, we have to compare it with an *average* value as we illustrated in Example (1) on page 177. Our degrees of freedom in the present example are:

(Boys) d.f. $= N_1 - 1 = 72 - 1 = 71$

(Girls) d.f. $= N_2 - 1 = 65 - 1 = 64$

In point of fact, averaging with such large degrees of freedom makes very little difference to our calculation. In the present example our averaged t value at the 5% level is 2.00 and 2.65 at the 1% level. Our obtained value of 6.09 exceeds both of these. We therefore reject the null hypothesis and conclude that there is a significant difference between the mean arithmetic scores of the boys and girls in our samples.

Example 3 Using the Mann Whitney U Test

For small samples ($N < 8$).

Suppose the following scores are collected from two groups of subjects. Is there a significant difference between the groups? Our null hypothesis (H_0) in this case is that the two groups of scores do not differ.

Table 58 Group A and Group B Scores

Group A	Group B
4	2
6	9
5	7
12	3
10	
7	
$N_A = 6$	$N_B = 4$

In assessing the difference between two independent samples, the Mann Whitney U Test provides a useful non parametric alternative to the t-test for uncor-

Statistics for Education and Physical Education

related data when the assumptions of the t-test are not met. It must be made clear however that the Mann Whitney U Test is used to evaluate the difference between population distributions, *not* the difference between population means. With this test, therefore, it is possible to obtain a significant difference between groups when the means are, in fact, identical. However, when the distributions of two groups are similar, as is generally the case in most experiments at student level, the Mann Whitney U Test does compare the central tendencies of the groups.

PROCEDURES FOR COMPUTING MANN WHITNEY U

1 Arrange the scores in order of their size and identify the group from which they are drawn.

Thus:

Scores	2	3	4	5	6	7	7	9	10	12
Group	B	B	A	A	A	B	A	B	A	A

2 Determine U by counting how many scores from Group A precede (are lower than) *each* Group B score.

e.g. For B score 3, no A scores precede it.

For B score 9, four scores precede it.

$U = 0 + 0 + 3 + 4 = 7$

3 Determine U by counting how many scores from Group B precede each Group A score.

$U = 2 + 2 + 2 + 2 + 4 + 4$

$U = 16$

4 Using the smaller value of $U = 7$, consult the table in Appendix 7 to determine its significance. That table shows N_L, the group with the larger number of scores (in our case, Group A in Table 58), and N_S, the group with the smaller number of scores, in our example, Group B in Table 58.

Enter the table in Appendix 7 in the top part of that table for $p = 0.05$ along the top line for N_L and down the side for N_S. At the intersection of $N_L = 6$ and $N_S = 4$, the obtained value is 2. The value of U must be equal to or smaller than the value shown in the table to be significant. Our value of 7 is in excess of the value shown. We therefore accept the null hypothesis and conclude that there is no significant difference between the groups.

Example 4

For moderately large samples (N_2 between 9 and 20).

As part of a survey of children's fitness it was decided to test whether children living in a rural environment were fitter than children living in an urban environment. Two random samples, one from each environment, were selected and measured on a fitness test battery. The null hypothesis (H_0) in this case is that rural and urban children's fitness scores do not differ.

Table 59   Urban and Rural Children's Fitness Scores

Urban children	Rural children
Fitness scores ($N_1 = 10$)	Fitness scores ($N_2 = 15$)
110	115
112	112
97	109
104	112
110	117
98	101
114	106 ·
100	118
104	119·
99	95
	116
	114·
	105
	110
	120

PROCEDURES FOR COMPUTING MANN WHITNEY U

Although the method employed in the previous example can be used, it becomes rather tedious as sample sizes increase.

The following method is therefore recommended.

1   Rank all the scores as though they are in one group, giving rank 1 to the lowest score.

   To those ranks which are tied, assign the average of the tied ranks.

Table 60 Rank Ordering of Urban and Rural Children's Fitness Scores

Urban children		Rural children	
Score	Rank	Score	Rank
110	13	115	20
112	16	112	16
97	2	109	11
104	7.5	112	16
110	13	117	22
98	3	101	6
114	18.5	106	10
100	5	118	23
104	7.5	119	24
99	4	95	1
		116	21
		114	18.5
		105	9
		110	13
		120	25
$R_1 = 89.5$		$R_2 = 235.5$	

2 Sum the ranks for each group

$$R_1 = 89.5, \qquad R_2 = 235.5$$

3 Compute U from the formulae:

$$U = N_1 N_2 + \frac{N_1(N_1 + 1)}{2} - R_1 \qquad \textit{Formula A}$$

and

$$U = N_1 N_2 + \frac{N_2(N_2 + 1)}{2} - R_2 \qquad \textit{Formula B}$$

where R_1 = sum of ranks for group with N_1 subjects
R_2 = sum of ranks for group with N_2 subjects.

FOR FORMULA A

$$U = (10)(15) + \frac{10(10 + 1)}{2} - 89.5$$

$$= 115.5$$

FOR FORMULA B

$$U = (10)(15) + \frac{15(15 + 1)}{2} - 235.5$$

$$= 34.5$$

We suggest rather than substitute into both formula A and formula B, if one U value is found and substituted into $U = N_1 N_2 - U'$, we get:

$$U = (10)(15) - 115.5$$
$$U = 34.5$$

4 We enter the table in Appendix 7 for the critical U values.

If the value of U in the table is *larger* than the smaller estimated value for the particular size of samples, then there is a significant difference between the groups.

Our lower value of $U = 34.5$ is smaller than the value $U = 39$ in the table for $N_S = 10$ and $N_L = 15$ at the 0.05 level. We therefore reject the null hypothesis and conclude that rural children have significantly higher fitness scores than urban children.

Example 5

For large samples $(N_2 > 20)$.

When one or both of the sample sizes are larger than 20, we convert our U value into a Z score, in order to interpret the significance. This is done using the formula:

$$Z = \frac{U - \dfrac{N_1 N_2}{2}}{\sqrt{\dfrac{(N_1)(N_2)(N_1 + N_2 + 1)}{12}}}$$

Having obtained our Z value, we then use Table 72 (page 198) to find the probability of its occurrence under the normal curve.

The power efficiency of the Mann Whitney U Test relative to the parametric t-test for independent samples is reported as 95.5% (Gibbons 1976).

Example 6   Using the Kolmogorov-Smirnov Two Sample Test

The final degree classifications awarded to 109 Physical Education students are further categorized on the basis of the students' A-level choices of 'Science' or 'Non-Science' subjects. We wish to examine the possibility that choice of A-level subjects is associated with final degree classification. The null hypothesis in this case is that there is no relationship between A-level choices ('Science' or 'Non-Science') and the final degree results.

The Kolmogorov-Smirnov Two Sample Test is appropriate to our problem. The assumptions governing the Kolmogorov-Smirnov Two Sample Test are similar to those we outlined in connection with the One Sample Test. The Kolmogorov-Smirnov Two Sample Test is used with nominal data grouped in continuous categories, or arranged in rank order form. Comparisons are made between two cumulative frequency distributions as in the One Sample Test. In the Two Sample Test however, both distributions are *observed*, rather than one *observed* and one *theoretical or expected*.

Table 61   Physical Education Degree Results

	2nd class upper	2nd class lower	3rd class	Pass	Fail	Sample size
Group 1 Science 'A' levels (F_1)	10	28	2	1	1	42
Group 2 No science 'A' levels (F_2)	6	55	6	0	0	67

PROCEDURES IN COMPUTING THE KOLMOGOROV-SMIRNOV TWO SAMPLE TEST

1   Convert the frequencies (F) in Table 61 to cumulative frequencies (CF) by serially adding

Table 62   Cumulative Frequency Table

Group 1 CF_1	10	38	40	41	42
Group 2 CF_2	6	61	67	67	67

2 Estimate the cumulative frequency proportions (CP) by dividing by the sample size and determine the absolute difference (D) between the cumulative proportions within each interval. Ignore minus signs.

Table 63   Cumulative Frequency Proportions

Group 1 CP_1	(10/42) 0.23	(38/42) 0.90	(40/42) 0.95	(41/42) 0.97	(42/42) 1.00
Group 2 CP_2	(6/67) 0.08	(61/67) 0.91	(67/67) 1.00	(67/67) 1.00	(67/67) 1.00
$D = \lvert CP_1 - CP_2 \rvert$	0.15	0.01	0.05	0.03	0

3 Identify the largest of the differences D

$$D = \lvert (CP_1 - CP_2) \rvert_{\text{MAX}} = 0.15$$

4 Compute K

$$K = D \sqrt{\frac{n_1 n_2}{n_1 + n_2}}$$

where n_1 = number of students with Science background
and n_2 = number of students without Science background.

$$K = 0.15 \sqrt{\frac{(42)(67)}{42 + 67}}$$
$$= 0.15\sqrt{25.81} = 0.76$$

5   Consult Table 64 below to the significance of K. If the obtained K is larger than the value in the table it is significant at that level.

Table 64   Critical Values of K

One-tailed test	0.05	0.025	0.01	0.001
Two-tailed test	0.1	0.05	0.02	0.002
K	1.22	1.36	1.51	1.86

Source: R. Meddis, *Statistical Handbook for Non-Statisticians*, London: McGraw-Hill, 1975, p. 62, with the kind permission of the author and publisher.

We see that our value of 0.76 is less than the value in the table of 1.22 at the 0.05 level, for a two-tailed test. We therefore accept the null hypothesis and conclude that there is no difference between the two groups in terms of their final degree classifications.

Siegel (1956) suggests that for small samples the Kolmogorov-Smirnov Test relative to the t-test has a power efficiency of approximately 96% and compared with the χ^2 two sample test is more powerful in all cases.

Example 7 Using χ^2, Chi Square $(2 \times k)$

In Table 65 below we report data to do with boys' preferences for various Physical Education activities, the boys being differentiated in terms of the secondary schools they attend.

We wish to find out whether there is a significant difference in the range of choices recorded by the two groups. The null hypothesis (H_0) in this case is that physical education preferences and type of school are not related.

Table 65 Boys' Physical Education Activity Preferences

	Games	Swimming	Gymnastics	Dance	Outdoor pursuits	
Public school	50	15	15	5	15	(100)
Comprehensive school	70	40	40	20	30	(200)

The χ^2 test is appropriate to our problem. Our data are in the form of frequencies that fall into discrete categories and are at the nominal level of measurement. The assumptions that are made in applying chi square to our data are that the two groups are independent, that the subjects in each group are randomly and independently selected and, as we noted earlier, that our observations fall into discrete categories. One further assumption in using chi square is to do with the value of expected frequencies, a term we explain below. Sample sizes have to be reasonably large in applying the χ^2 test, such as that no expected frequency is less than 5 when rows (r) or columns (c) exceed 2, or less than 10 when rows (r) or columns (c) equal 2.

The chi square technique tests whether an *observed frequency* distribution is sufficiently close to an expected frequency distribution to have occurred under the null hypothesis.

χ^2 is given by the formula:

$$\chi^2 = \sum \frac{(O - E)^2}{E}$$

where O = the observed frequencies
 E = the expected frequencies
 $\sum$ = the sum of.

Statistics for Education and Physical Education

PROCEDURES FOR COMPUTING χ^2

1 Set out the observed frequency distributions as shown below.

Observed frequencies

	Games	Swimming	Gymnastics	Dance	Outdoor pursuits	
Public school	50	15	15	5	15	(100)
Comprehensive school	70	40	40	20	30	(200)
	(120)	(55)	(55)	(25)	(45)	N = 300

2 Compute the *expected* frequencies (*E*) for each cell by multiplying the column and the row total for that cell and dividing by *N*. By way of example, take the cell at the intersection of column Games and row Public School. The *expected frequency* is given by:

$$\frac{120 \times 100}{300} = 40$$

Similarly, for the cell at the intersection of column Gymnastics and row Comprehensive, the expected frequency is given by:

$$\frac{55 \times 200}{300} = 36.7$$

The expected frequencies for each cell are set out below.

Expected frequencies

	Games	Swimming	Gymnastics	Dance	Outdoor pursuits
Public school	40	18.3	18.3	8.3	15
Comprehensive school	80	36.7	36.7	16.7	30

188

3   For each cell, compute

$$\frac{(O - E)^2}{E}$$

	Games	Swimming	Gymnastics	Dance	Outdoor pursuits
Public school	2.5	0.59	0.59	1.31	0.0
Comprehensive school	1.25	0.29	0.29	0.65	0.0

$$\chi^2 = \sum \frac{(O - E)^2}{E}$$
$$= 2.5 + 1.25 + 0.59 + 0.29 + 0.59 + 0.29 + 1.31 + 0.65$$
$$= 7.47$$

4   Before we can determine the significance of our chi square value of 6.59 we must obtain the appropriate degrees of freedom. Degrees of freedom are given by the formula:

$$\text{d.f.} = (r - 1)(c - 1)$$
$$= (2 - 1)(5 - 1)$$
$$= 4$$

Consulting the table in Appendix 2 we see that at d.f. = 4 a value of 9.49 is required for significance at the 0.05 level. Since our obtained value fails to reach this we accept the null hypothesis and conclude that there are no significant differences between our public school and comprehensive school subjects' choices of physical education activities.

10.7 Two Group – Before and After Design. One Group as Control Group

Group	Before treatment observations $X_{(b)}$	After treatment observations $X_{(a)}$
1 Subjects A	$X_{A(b)}$	$X_{A(a)}$
B	$X_{B(b)}$	$X_{B(a)}$
C	$X_{C(b)}$	$X_{C(a)}$
D	$X_{D(b)}$	$X_{D(a)}$
	Control (no treatment)	
2 Subjects E	$X_{E(b)}$	$X_{E(a)}$
F	$X_{F(b)}$	$X_{F(a)}$
G	$X_{G(b)}$	$X_{G(a)}$
H	$X_{H(b)}$	$X_{H(a)}$

Example 1 Using t Tests for Correlated Means

A Maths teacher who has been introduced to a novel method of teaching differential equations decides to test the effectiveness of the new approach with his secondary school group of 18 pupils. First, he randomly assigns the students to two groups, one of which he designates the experimental group (E), the other the control group (C).

Before teaching the new process to E, he obtains a measure of each student's ability on differential equations. Having taught the new approach to E, but not to C, he then gives a parallel test on differential equations to the whole class.

The data are set out in Tables 66 and 67 below.

Table 66 Experimental Group (E) Before and After Treatment Scores

Pupil	Before treatment scores $X_{(b)}$	After treatment scores $X_{(a)}$
1	35	29
2	41	49
3	64	73
4	28	27
5	39	45
6	50	61
7	56	65
8	71	77
9	29	33

Table 67 Control Group (C) Before and After Scores

Pupil	Before scores $X_{(b)}$	After scores $X_{(a)}$
10	27	20
11	65	66
12	47	42
13	28	32
14	70	72
15	38	42
16	45	44
17	57	58
18	29	32

Statistics for Education and Physical Education

We wish to find out how the teaching programme affects the post-treatment scores of Group E. The null hypothesis (H_0) in this case is that post treatment scores in Groups E and C do not differ from their respective pre-treatment scores. t tests for correlated means are appropriate to our problem.

The assumptions for using a t test for correlated means are that the data are in the form of pairs of scores which are randomly sampled and that the data are at the interval level of measurement.

t test for correlated means is given by:

$$t = \frac{\sum D}{\sqrt{\dfrac{N \sum D^2 - (\sum D)^2}{N - 1}}}$$

where D is obtained by taking the 'before' treatment score from the 'after' treatment score, and N is the number of subjects.

PROCEDURES FOR COMPUTING t FOR CORRELATED MEANS

1 Cast the data into a table such as the one illustrating our example below.
2 Compute D for each subject by subtracting the 'before' treatment score from the 'after' treatment score.
3 Compute D^2 for each subject by squaring his D value.
4 Sum the D values algebraically to give $\sum D$.
5 Sum the D^2 values to give $\sum D^2$.

Table 68   Group E. Comparison of Before Treatment and After Treatment Scores (Example 1)

Pupil	Before treatment scores $X_{(b)}$	After treatment scores $X_{(a)}$	$D(X_{(a)} - X_{(b)})$	D^2
1	35	29	-6	36
2	41	49	$+8$	64
3	64	73	$+9$	81
4	28	27	-1	1
5	39	45	$+6$	36
6	50	61	$+11$	121
7	56	65	$+9$	81
8	71	77	$+6$	36
9	29	33	$+4$	16
			$\sum D = 46$	$\sum D^2 = 472$

6 Substitute the values N, D, $\sum D^2$, and $(\sum D)^2$ into the formula.

$$t = \cfrac{\sum D}{\sqrt{\cfrac{N \sum D^2 - (\sum D)^2}{N - 1}}}$$

Substituting from Table 68

$$t = \cfrac{46}{\sqrt{\cfrac{9(472) - (46)^2}{8}}} = \frac{46}{16.32} = 2.82$$

We repeat the above computations with the data for the Control Group C.

Table 69   Group C. Comparison of Before and After Scores

Pupil	Before scores $X_{(b)}$	After scores $X_{(a)}$	$D(X_{(a)} - X_{(b)})$	D^2
10	27	20	−7	49
11	65	66	+1	1
12	47	42	−5	25
13	28	32	+4	16
14	70	72	+2	4
15	38	42	+4	16
16	45	44	−1	1
17	57	58	+1	1
18	29	32	+3	9
			$\sum D = 2$	$\sum D^2 = 122$

Substituting from Table 69

$$t = \cfrac{2}{\sqrt{\cfrac{9(122) - (2)^2}{7}}} = \frac{2}{11.69} = 0.17$$

To find the significance of t for the Experimental and the Control Group analyses, we must first determine the number of degrees of freedom for each group.

d.f. is given by $N - 1$.

Group E   d.f. $= 9 - 1 = 8$

Group C   d.f. $= 9 - 1 = 8$

Looking first at Group E's result ($t = 2.82$). We enter the table in Appendix 3 at d.f. $= 8$. Because the teacher in our example makes no prediction as to whether the new method will effect changes in one direction or the other, a two-tailed test is appropriate.

We see that at $p = 0.05$, a value of $t = 2.31$ is significant. Our obtained value ($t = 2.82$) is in excess of that value. We therefore reject the null hypothesis and conclude that Group E makes a significant improvement on the second test on differential equations.

Looking now at Group C's result ($t = 0.17$). Entering the table in Appendix 3 we see that at $p = 0.05$, a t value of 2.31 is significant. Our obtained value ($t = 0.17$) falls short of that value. We therefore accept the null hypothesis and conclude that no significant improvement occurs in Group C on the second test on differential equations.

Taking the performances of Groups E and C together, our Maths teacher may express cautious optimism in the new method he has tried out, that is, he may reject the null hypothesis. He should reserve judgement about its effectiveness however, until he has obtained similar results in further replications of the experiment.

Example 2   Using the Wilcoxon Test for Two Correlated Samples

An alternative way of examining the data in Tables 68 and 69 is by means of the Wilcoxon Test for Two Correlated Samples, sometimes referred to as the Wilcoxon Matched-Pairs Signed-Ranks Test.

The assumptions for using the Wilcoxon Test are less restrictive than those applying to the t test for correlated means. With the Wilcoxon Test, the data must be in the form of pairs of scores which are randomly-sampled and data should be at least at the ordinal level of measurement.

With samples (i.e. pairs of scores or observations) less than 25, T, the critical value employed in the Wilcoxon Test can be obtained from Table 71 set out below. We deal first with the procedures for small samples. We then go on to outline the formula for use when $N \geq 25$.

PROCEDURES FOR COMPUTING WILCOXON T WITH SAMPLES < 25

1   Cast the data into a table such as the one illustrating our example below.
2   Compute d, the differences between the 'before' and 'after' treatment scores. Enter in Column 1.
3   Now enter in Column 2 the absolute differences between the scores, $|d|$.
4   Rank $|d|$ by assigning 1 to the lowest absolute difference, 2 to the next lowest and so on.

5 With tied $|d|$ values, the ties are assigned the average rank that they would have obtained had there been no ties.

6 Where a pair of observations are assigned 0 for $|d|$, that pair is then dropped from the analysis, thus reducing the total N.

7 In the last column (Column 4) the rank difference recorded in Column 3 is now given the algebraic sign of the differences recorded in Column 1.

8 Total the ranks having positive signs $(+)$. Label $T+$.

9 Total the ranks having negative signs $(-)$. Label $T-$.

10 In the Wilcoxon Test, it is the smaller of $T+$ and $T-$ which we compare with the critical values of T shown in Table 71. Where $T+$ and $T-$ are similar in value, we can infer that the two groups, or pairs of scores are similar. The more dissimilar the two groups, the greater the difference between $T+$ and $T-$.

11 We enter Table 71 at N, the number of pairs of scores or observations. Our obtained T must be smaller than the value given in the table to be significant.

Example The data from the Experimental Group taught differential equations by a novel method are used to illustrate the application of the Wilcoxon Test for Two Correlated Samples.

Table 70 Group E. Comparison of Before Treatment and After Treatment Scores (Example 2)

Pupil	Before treatment scores $X_{(b)}$	After treatment scores $X_{(a)}$	Col. 1 d	Col. 2 $|d|$	Col. 3 rank difference	Col. 4 signed rank difference
1	35	29	6	6	4	4
2	41	49	-8	8	6	-6
3	64	73	-9	9	7.5	-7.5
4	28	27	1	1	1	1
5	39	45	-6	6	4	-4
6	50	61	-11	11	9	-9
7	56	65	-9	9	7.5	-7.5
8	71	77	-6	6	4	-4
9	29	33	-4	4	2	-2
					$T+ = 5$	
					$T- = 40$	

195

Statistics for Education and Physical Education

Entering Table 71 at $N = 9$ we see that a T value equal to or less than 5 is required for significance. Our obtained value of $T = 5$ is equal to that critical value. We therefore reject the null hypothesis and conclude that there is a significant difference ($p = 0.05$) between the 'before' and 'after' scores of the pupils who were taught a novel method of solving differential equations, a result, we might note, that is in line with our previous analysis by t test for correlated means (Table 68, page 192).

PROCEDURES FOR COMPUTING THE WILCOXON TEST FOR TWO CORRELATED SAMPLES WHEN $N \geq 25$

When N, the number of paired observations or scores, is greater than 25 it has been shown that T, the sum of the ranks is normally distributed.

The following formula is therefore applied:

$$Z = \frac{T - \dfrac{N(N + 1)}{4}}{\sqrt{\dfrac{N(N + 1)(2N + 1)}{24}}}$$

where T is (as before) the smaller of the $T+$, $T-$ values and N is the number of paired scores or observations. Z values are interpreted by reference to Table 72.

It has been shown (Siegel, 1956, pages 79–80) that the above formula gives an excellent approximation even for samples as small as in Table 71.

We recompute our data from Table 70 using the Wilcoxon Test formula for large samples.

$$Z = \frac{T - \dfrac{N(N + 1)}{4}}{\sqrt{\dfrac{N(N + 1)(2N + 1)}{24}}} = \frac{5 - \dfrac{9 \times (10)}{4}}{\sqrt{\dfrac{9(10)(19)}{24}}}$$

$$= \frac{-17.5}{8.44} = -2.07$$

From Table 72 we see that the probability of a Z value of -2.07 occurring by chance is $p = 2 \times (0.0192) = 0.038$ for a two-tailed test. Once again, therefore, we reject the null hypothesis.

Table 71 Critical Values of T in the Wilcoxon Test for Two Correlated Samples

Sample size	Levels of significance			
	One-tailed test			
	0.05	0.025	0.01	0.001
	Two-tailed test			
	0.1	0.05	0.02	0.002
$N = 5$	$T \leq 0$			
6	2	0		
7	3	2	0	
8	5	3	1	
9	8	5	3	
10	10	8	5	0
11	13	10	7	1
12	17	13	9	2
13	21	17	12	4
14	25	21	15	6
15	30	25	19	8
16	35	29	23	11
17	41	34	27	14
18	47	40	32	18
19	53	46	37	21
20	60	52	43	26
21	67	58	49	30
22	75	65	55	35
23	83	73	62	40
24	91	81	69	45
25	100	89	76	51
26	110	98	84	58
27	119	107	92	64
28	130	116	101	71
30	151	137	120	86
31	163	147	130	94
32	175	159	140	103
33	187	170	151	112

Source: Adapted from Table 6.5, Ray Meddis, *Statistical Handbook for Non-Statisticians*, London: McGraw-Hill, 1975, p. 113, with the kind permission of the author and publisher.

Table 72   Probabilities Associated with Values as Extreme as Observed Value of Z in the Normal Curve of Distribution

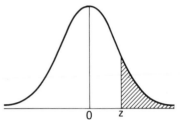

z	0.00	0.01	0.02	0.03	0.04	0.05	0.06	0.07	0.08	0.09
0.0	0.5000	0.4960	0.4920	0.4880	0.4840	0.4801	0.4761	0.4721	0.4681	0.4641
0.1	0.4602	0.4562	0.4522	0.4483	0.4443	0.4404	0.4364	0.4325	0.4286	0.4247
0.2	0.4207	0.4168	0.4129	0.4090	0.4052	0.4013	0.3974	0.3936	0.3897	0.3859
0.3	0.3821	0.3783	0.3745	0.3707	0.3669	0.3632	0.3594	0.3557	0.3520	0.3483
0.4	0.3446	0.3409	0.3372	0.3336	0.3300	0.3264	0.3228	0.3192	0.3156	0.3121
0.5	0.3085	0.3050	0.3015	0.2981	0.2946	0.2912	0.2877	0.2843	0.2810	0.2776
0.6	0.2743	0.2709	0.2676	0.2643	0.2611	0.2578	0.2546	0.2514	0.2483	0.2451
0.7	0.2420	0.2389	0.2358	0.2327	0.2296	0.2266	0.2236	0.2206	0.2177	0.2148
0.8	0.2119	0.2090	0.2061	0.2033	0.2005	0.1977	0.1949	0.1922	0.1894	0.1867
0.9	0.1841	0.1814	0.1788	0.1762	0.1736	0.1711	0.1685	0.1660	0.1635	0.1611
1.0	0.1587	0.1562	0.1539	0.1515	0.1492	0.1469	0.1446	0.1423	0.1401	0.1379
1.1	0.1357	0.1335	0.1314	0.1292	0.1271	0.1251	0.1230	0.1210	0.1190	0.1170
1.2	0.1151	0.1131	0.1112	0.1093	0.1075	0.1056	0.1038	0.1020	0.1003	0.0985
1.3	0.0968	0.0951	0.0934	0.0918	0.0901	0.0885	0.0869	0.0853	0.0838	0.0823
1.4	0.0808	0.0793	0.0778	0.0764	0.0749	0.0735	0.0721	0.0708	0.0694	0.0681
1.5	0.0668	0.0655	0.0643	0.0630	0.0618	0.0606	0.0594	0.0582	0.0571	0.0559
1.6	0.0548	0.0537	0.0526	0.0516	0.0505	0.0495	0.0485	0.0475	0.0465	0.0455
1.7	0.0446	0.0436	0.0427	0.0418	0.0409	0.0401	0.0392	0.0384	0.0375	0.0367
1.8	0.0359	0.0351	0.0344	0.0336	0.0329	0.0322	0.0314	0.0307	0.0301	0.0294
1.9	0.0287	0.0281	0.0274	0.0268	0.0262	0.0256	0.0250	0.0244	0.0239	0.0233

Read values of Z to one decimal place down the left hand column *Column z*. Read across *Row z* for values to two decimal places. The probabilities contained in the table are *one-tailed*. For two-tailed tests, multiply by 2.

Table 72 Probabilities Associated with Values as Extreme as Observed Value of Z in the Normal Curve of Distribution (continued)

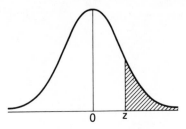

z	0.00	0.01	0.02	0.03	0.04	0.05	0.06	0.07	0.08	0.09
2.0	0.0228	0.0222	0.0217	0.0212	0.0207	0.0202	0.0197	0.0192	0.0188	0.0183
2.1	0.0179	0.0174	0.0170	0.0166	0.0162	0.0158	0.0154	0.0150	0.0146	0.0143
2.2	0.0139	0.0136	0.0132	0.0129	0.0125	0.0122	0.0119	0.0116	0.0113	0.0110
2.3	0.0107	0.0104	0.0102	0.0099	0.0096	0.0094	0.0091	0.0089	0.0087	0.0084
2.4	0.0082	0.0080	0.0078	0.0075	0.0073	0.0071	0.0069	0.0068	0.0066	0.0064
2.5	0.0062	0.0060	0.0059	0.0057	0.0055	0.0054	0.0052	0.0051	0.0049	0.0048
2.6	0.0047	0.0045	0.0044	0.0043	0.0041	0.0040	0.0039	0.0038	0.0037	0.0036
2.7	0.0035	0.0034	0.0033	0.0032	0.0031	0.0030	0.0029	0.0028	0.0027	0.0026
2.8	0.0026	0.0025	0.0024	0.0023	0.0023	0.0022	0.0021	0.0021	0.0020	0.0019
2.9	0.0019	0.0018	0.0018	0.0017	0.0016	0.0016	0.0015	0.0015	0.0014	0.0014
3.0	0.0013	0.0013	0.0013	0.0012	0.0012	0.0011	0.0011	0.0011	0.0010	0.0010
3.1	0.0010	0.0009	0.0009	0.0009	0.0008	0.0008	0.0008	0.0008	0.0007	0.0007
3.2	0.0007									
3.3	0.0005									
3.4	0.0003									
3.5	0.00023									
3.6	0.00016									
3.7	0.00011									
3.8	0.00007									
3.9	0.00005									
4.0	0.00003									

Examples

(i) The probability of a $Z \geq 0.14$ on a one-tailed test is $p = 0.4443$.

(ii) The probability of a $Z \geq 1.98$ on a two-tailed test is $p = 2 \times (0.0239) = 0.0478$.

10.8 Multi Group Research Design: More than Two Groups, One Single Variable

Group 1 subjects A, B, C, D	Group 2 subjects E, F, G, H	Group 3 subjects J, K, L, M	Group 4 subjects N, O, P, Q
X_1 X_a	X_2 X_e	X_3 X_j	X_4 X_n
X_b	X_f	X_k	X_o
X_c	X_g	X_l	X_p
X_d	X_h	X_m	X_q

Example 1 Using One-Way Analysis of Variance, Independent Samples (Fixed Effects, Completely Randomized Model)

The One-Way Analysis of Variance for independent samples is the most commonly-used technique for examining the differences between two or more group means. It involves testing the difference between means of random samples taken from the population(s) of specific interest. The reader is advised to refer to page 161 for a brief explanation of the rationale behind analysis of variance techniques before proceeding to the example that follows.

Suppose that in an experiment to determine the effect of training on the body's ability to utilize oxygen, three groups of ten physical education students are selected at random. Two of the groups are given different training programmes and the third undertakes no training at all.

Do the following maximum oxygen uptake measures indicate that the training programmes have an effect on the body's ability to utilize oxygen?

The null hypothesis (H_0) in this case is that training programmes have no effect on the body's ability to utilize oxygen.

Table 73   Oxygen Uptake Measures

Independent variable (training)		
Training method 1 (Group 1)	Training method 2 (Group 2)	No training (Group 3)
4.0	3.2	1.8
3.4	2.6	2.7
3.2	2.4	3.2
4.5	3.7	3.0
4.2	3.4	3.2
4.9	4.1	1.8
3.7	3.3	2.9
5.0	3.3	3.3
3.9	3.1	2.6
4.2	3.4	3.5
Group means 4.1	3.25	2.8

The assumptions of analysis of variance are that our data are at the interval or ratio level of measurement, that our samples are drawn at random, and the variances of the sample populations are equal. It is common practice in using

Statistics for Education and Physical Education

analysis of variance to check this last assumption by means of a simple test of homogeneity of variance. This involves computing individual variances in respect of the sub groups in each of our cells and then dividing the largest variance by the smallest. The result of this division is treated as an F value and interpreted in the usual way by means of the F table. If this obtained F value is not statistically significant we may proceed on the assumption that the variances of the sampled populations are homogeneous and complete the analysis of variance. Our test of the homogeneity of variance in respect of the data in our example is set out below.

HOMOGENEITY OF VARIANCE CHECK

Variance is given by the formula:

$$\text{Var} = \frac{\sum X^2 - \frac{(\sum X)^2}{n}}{n-1}$$

1 Square each score (X^2) and total the scores $(\sum X)$ and squares of scores $(\sum X^2)$ for each group. Enter in a separate data Table 74.

Table 74 One-Way Analysis of Variance for Independent Samples (Fixed Effects, Completely Randomized Model)

Training method 1 (Group 1)		Training method 2 (Group 2)		No training (Group 3)	
X_1	X_1^2	X_2	X_2^2	X_3	X_3^2
4.0	16.00	3.2	10.24	1.8	3.24
3.4	11.56	2.6	6.76	2.7	7.29
3.2	10.24	2.4	5.76	3.2	10.24
4.5	20.25	3.7	13.69	3.0	9.00
4.2	17.64	3.4	11.56	3.2	10.24
4.9	24.01	4.1	16.81	1.8	3.24
3.7	13.69	3.3	10.89	2.9	8.41
5.0	25.00	3.3	10.89	3.3	10.89
3.9	15.21	3.1	9.61	2.6	6.76
4.2	17.64	3.4	11.56	3.5	12.25
$\sum X_1 =$ 41.00	$\sum X_1^2 =$ 171.24	$\sum X_2 =$ 32.5	$\sum X_2^2 =$ 107.77	$\sum X_3 =$ 28.0	$\sum X_3^2 =$ 81.56

2 Calculate Variance for each group.

Group 1.

$$Var = \frac{\sum X_1^2 - \frac{(\sum X_1)^2}{n_1}}{n_1 - 1}$$

$$= \frac{171.24 - \frac{(41)^2}{10}}{10 - 1} = \frac{171.24 - 168.1}{9}$$

$$= 0.34$$

where n_1 = number in group 1.

Group 2.

$$Var = \frac{\sum X_2^2 - \frac{(\sum X_2)^2}{n_2}}{n_2 - 1}$$

$$= \frac{107.77 - \frac{(32.5)^2}{10}}{10 - 1} = \frac{107.77 - 105.63}{9}$$

$$= 0.23$$

Group 3.

$$Var = \frac{\sum X_3^2 - \frac{(\sum X_3)^2}{n_3}}{n_3 - 1}$$

$$= \frac{81.56 - \frac{(28)^2}{10}}{10 - 1} = \frac{81.56 - 78.4}{9}$$

$$= 0.35$$

3 Compute F_{max}.

$$F_{max} = \frac{\text{Largest variance}}{\text{Smallest variance}}$$

$$= \frac{0.35}{0.23} = 1.52$$

4 Consult the table in Appendix 4 for d.f. = $n_3 - 1 = 9$ and d.f. = $n_2 - 1 = 9$ to determine the significance of F_{max}.

Statistics for Education and Physical Education

We see that our obtained value of 1.52 is smaller than the value in the table at the 0.05 level ($F = 3.18$). We therefore accept the null hypothesis that there is no significant difference between our sub group variances. We may therefore proceed with our one-way analysis of variance.

The reader should note that although a check on the homogeneity of variance is recommended, when samples are sufficiently large and contain equal numbers, the results of an analysis of variance will not be greatly affected by unequal variances in sub groups.

VARIANCE ANALYSIS

The total variance in this independent sample, randomized design can be partitioned into:

Systematic Effects

1 BETWEEN GROUPS (treatments or conditions) variance is the variance between group means caused by the independent variable, which in this case is the different training programmes.

Error Effects

2 WITHIN GROUPS variance is the variance due to subject differences and uncontrolled factors.

$$F_{\text{BETWEEN GROUPS}} = \frac{\text{Between groups variance}}{\text{Within groups variance}}$$

1 Calculate the Grand Total (GT).

$$GT = \frac{(\sum X)^2}{N} = \frac{(\sum X_1 + \sum X_2 + \sum X_3)^2}{N}$$

$$= \frac{(41 + 32.5 + 28)^2}{30}$$

$$= \frac{(101.5)^2}{30} = 343.4$$

$\sum X$ = sum of all raw scores
and N = total number of scores.

2 Compute the TOTAL sum of squares (SS_{TOTAL}).

$$SS_{\text{TOTAL}} = \sum X^2 - GT = [\sum X_1^2 + \sum X_2^2 + \sum X_3^2] - GT$$
$$= [171.24 + 107.77 + 81.56] - 343.4$$
$$= 360.57 - 343.4 = 17.17$$

where $\sum X^2$ = sum of squares of all raw scores.

3 Compute the BETWEEN GROUPS sum of squares (SS_{BETWEEN}).

$$SS_{\text{BETWEEN}} = \frac{(\sum X_1)^2}{n_1} + \frac{(\sum X_2)^2}{n_2} + \frac{(\sum X_3)^2}{n_3} - GT$$

$$= \frac{(41)^2}{10} + \frac{(32.5)^2}{10} + \frac{(28)^2}{10} - 343.4$$

$$= 352.13 - 343.4 = 8.73$$

4 Compute the WITHIN GROUPS sum of squares (SS_{WITHIN}).

For Group 1:

$$SS_{\text{W}} = \sum X_1^2 - \frac{(\sum X_1)^2}{n_1}$$

$$= 171.24 - 168.1 = 3.14$$

For Group 2:

$$SS_{\text{W}} = \sum X_2^2 - \frac{(\sum X_2)^2}{n_2}$$

$$= 107.77 - 105.63 = 2.14$$

For Group 3:

$$SS_{\text{W}} = \sum X_3^2 - \frac{(\sum X_3)^2}{n_3}$$

$$= 81.56 - 78.4 = 3.16$$

The total of these gives the within groups sum of squares.

$$SS_{\text{WITHIN}} = 3.14 + 2.14 + 3.16$$

$$= 8.44$$

5 Determine the degrees of freedom for each sum of squares.

d.f. for $SS_{\text{TOTAL}} = (N - 1) = (30 - 1) = 29$

where N = number of scores

d.f. for $SS_{\text{BETWEEN}} = (k - 1) = (3 - 1) = 2$

where k = number of groups

d.f. for $SS_{\text{WITHIN}} = (N - k) = (30 - 3) = 27$

6 Estimate the variances.

$$\text{Var} = \frac{\text{Sum of squares}}{\text{d.f.}}$$

$$\text{Var}_{\text{BETWEEN}} = \frac{SS_{\text{BETWEEN}}}{d.f._{\text{BETWEEN}}} = \frac{8.73}{2} = 4.36$$

$$\text{Var}_{\text{WITHIN}} = \frac{SS_{\text{WITHIN}}}{d.f._{\text{WITHIN}}} = \frac{8.44}{27} = 0.31$$

7 Compute F

$$F = \frac{\text{Between groups variance}}{\text{Within groups variance}} = \frac{4.36}{0.31} = 14.06$$

8 Enter results in an Analysis of Variance Table.

Table 75 Analysis of Variance Table

Source of variation	Sum of squares	d.f.	Variance	F
Between groups	8.73	2	$\dfrac{8.73}{2} = 4.36$	14.06
Within groups	8.44	27	$\dfrac{8.44}{27} = 0.31$	
Total	17.17	29		

9 Determine the significance of F using the table in Appendix 4.

Our obtained value of $F = 14.06$ is larger than the values in the table at both the 0.05 $(F = 3.35)$ and the 0.01 $(F = 5.49)$ levels for d.f.'s = 2 and 27. We therefore reject the null hypothesis and conclude that there is a significant difference between group means.

Although we have found a significant difference between the means of the groups, we do not know if *all three* means differ from one another. The F test tells us that *at least* two differ, but does not identify which two.

In order to find out which of the means differ, we must apply a further statistical test to our data. This is called a Tukey test.

PROCEDURES FOR COMPUTING THE TUKEY TEST FOR COMPARING MEANS

1 Construct a table of sample mean differences.

Table 76 Comparison of Sample Mean Differences

	Comparison means	M_1	M_2	M_3
Group 1	$M_1 = 4.1$		$M_1 - M_2 = 0.85$	$M_1 - M_3 = 1.3$
Group 2	$M_2 = 3.25$			$M_2 - M_3 = 0.45$
Group 3	$M_3 = 2.8$			

2 Compute T

$$T = (q) \times \sqrt{\frac{\text{Var}_{\text{WITHIN}} \text{ (i.e. error variance)}}{N}}$$

where N = number in each group or the number of scores from which each mean is calculated.

The q value in the above formula is found by consulting Tables 77 and 78 and determining the value corresponding to the number of means (n in the Tukey table) and the degrees of freedom for the denominator of our prior F test. That denominator is, of course, the within groups variance and its appropriate degrees of freedom are read as V in the Tukey table.

We see that in our example, q at the 0.05 level = 3.51 (interpolated) when $n = 3$ and $V = 27$.

Thus

$$T_{0.05} = 3.51 \sqrt{\frac{0.31}{10}} = 0.62$$

If the T value of 0.62 is smaller than the difference between two means, then the means are significantly different. Referring to our table of mean differences, we see that there is a significant difference between the means of Group 1 and both of the other groups. There is no significant difference between the means of Group 2 and Group 3.

We therefore reject the null hypothesis and conclude that only training method 1 has an effect upon the body's ability to utilize oxygen.

Table 77 Tukey Test

Percentage Points (q) of the Studentized Range

$(p = 0.05)$

n = the total number of means being compared

v = degrees of freedom of denominator of F test

v \ n	2	3	4	5	6	7	8	9	10
1	17.97	26.98	32.82	37.08	40.41	43.12	45.40	47.36	49.07
2	6.08	8.33	9.80	10.88	11.74	12.44	13.03	13.54	13.99
3	4.50	5.91	6.82	7.50	8.04	8.48	8.85	9.18	9.46
4	3.93	5.04	5.76	6.29	6.71	7.05	7.35	7.60	7.83
5	3.64	4.60	5.22	5.67	6.03	6.33	6.58	6.80	6.99
6	3.46	4.34	4.90	5.30	5.63	5.90	6.12	6.32	6.49
7	3.34	4.16	4.68	5.06	5.36	5.61	5.82	6.00	6.16
8	3.26	4.04	4.53	4.89	5.17	5.40	5.60	5.77	5.92
9	3.20	3.95	4.41	4.76	5.02	5.24	5.43	5.59	5.74
10	3.15	3.88	4.33	4.65	4.91	5.12	5.30	5.46	5.60
11	3.11	3.82	4.26	4.57	4.82	5.03	5.20	5.35	5.49
12	3.08	3.77	4.20	4.51	4.75	4.95	5.12	5.27	5.39
13	3.06	3.73	4.15	4.45	4.69	4.88	5.05	5.19	5.32
14	3.03	3.70	4.11	4.41	4.64	4.83	4.99	5.13	5.25
15	3.01	3.67	4.08	4.37	4.59	4.78	4.94	5.08	5.20
16	3.00	3.65	4.05	4.33	4.56	4.74	4.90	5.03	5.15
17	2.98	3.63	4.02	4.30	4.52	4.70	4.86	4.99	5.11
18	2.97	3.61	4.00	4.28	4.49	4.67	4.82	4.96	5.07
19	2.96	3.59	3.98	4.25	4.47	4.65	4.79	4.92	5.04
20	2.95	3.58	3.96	4.23	4.45	4.62	4.77	4.90	5.01
24	2.92	3.53	3.90	4.17	4.37	4.54	4.68	4.81	4.92
30	2.89	3.49	3.85	4.10	4.30	4.46	4.60	4.72	4.82
40	2.86	3.44	3.79	4.04	4.23	4.39	4.52	4.63	4.73
60	2.83	3.40	3.74	3.98	4.16	4.31	4.44	4.55	4.65
120	2.80	3.36	3.68	3.92	4.10	4.24	4.36	4.47	4.56
∞	2.77	3.31	3.63	3.86	4.03	4.17	4.29	4.39	4.47

Source: From Pearson, E. S., and Hartley, H. O., editors; *Biometrika Tables for Statisticians*, ed. 3, vol. I. Cambridge: Cambridge Univ. Press, 1966, with the kind permission of the trustees and publishers.

Table 77   Tukey Test

Percentage Points (q) of the Studentized Range (continued)

$(p = 0.05)$
$n = $ the total number of means being compared
$v = $ degrees of freedom of denominator of F test

v \ n	11	12	13	14	15	16	17	18	19	20
1	50.59	51.96	53.20	54.33	55.36	56.32	57.22	58.04	58.83	59.56
2	14.39	14.75	15.08	15.38	15.65	15.91	16.14	16.37	16.57	16.77
3	9.72	9.95	10.15	10.35	10.52	10.69	10.84	10.98	11.11	11.24
4	8.03	8.21	8.37	8.52	8.66	8.79	8.91	9.03	9.13	9.23
5	7.17	7.32	7.47	7.60	7.72	7.83	7.93	8.03	8.12	8.21
6	6.65	6.79	6.92	7.03	7.14	7.24	7.34	7.43	7.51	7.59
7	6.30	6.43	6.55	6.66	6.76	6.85	6.94	7.02	7.10	7.17
8	6.05	6.18	6.29	6.39	6.48	6.57	6.65	6.73	6.80	6.87
9	5.87	5.98	6.09	6.19	6.28	6.36	6.44	6.51	6.58	6.64
10	5.72	5.83	5.93	6.03	6.11	6.19	6.27	6.34	6.40	6.47
11	5.61	5.71	5.81	5.90	5.98	6.06	6.13	6.20	6.27	6.33
12	5.51	5.61	5.71	5.80	5.88	5.95	6.02	6.09	6.15	6.21
13	5.43	5.53	5.63	5.71	5.79	5.86	5.93	5.99	6.05	6.11
14	5.36	5.46	5.55	5.64	5.71	5.79	5.85	5.91	5.97	6.03
15	5.31	5.40	5.49	5.57	5.65	5.72	5.78	5.85	5.90	5.96
16	5.26	5.35	5.44	5.52	5.59	5.66	5.73	5.79	5.84	5.90
17	5.21	5.31	5.39	5.47	5.54	5.61	5.67	5.73	5.79	5.84
18	5.17	5.27	5.35	5.43	5.50	5.57	5.63	5.69	5.74	5.79
19	5.14	5.23	5.31	5.39	5.46	5.53	5.59	5.65	5.70	5.75
20	5.11	5.20	5.28	5.36	5.43	5.49	5.55	5.61	5.66	5.71
24	5.01	5.10	5.18	5.25	5.32	5.38	5.44	5.49	5.55	5.59
30	4.92	5.00	5.08	5.15	5.21	5.27	5.33	5.38	5.43	5.47
40	4.82	4.90	4.98	5.04	5.11	5.16	5.22	5.27	5.31	5.36
60	4.73	4.81	4.88	4.94	5.00	5.06	5.11	5.15	5.20	5.24
120	4.64	4.71	4.78	4.84	4.90	4.95	5.00	5.04	5.09	5.13
∞	4.55	4.62	4.68	4.74	4.80	4.85	4.89	4.93	4.97	5.01

Table 78   Tukey Test

$(p = 0.01)$
n = the total number of means being compared
v = degrees of freedom of denominator of F test

v \ n	2	3	4	5	6	7	8	9	10
1	90.03	135.0	164.3	185.6	202.2	215.8	227.2	237.0	245.6
2	14.04	19.02	22.29	24.72	26.63	28.20	29.53	30.68	31.69
3	8.26	10.62	12.17	13.33	14.24	15.00	15.64	16.20	16.69
4	6.51	8.12	9.17	9.96	10.58	11.10	11.55	11.93	12.27
5	5.70	6.98	7.80	8.42	8.91	9.32	9.67	9.97	10.24
6	5.24	6.33	7.03	7.56	7.97	8.32	8.61	8.87	9.10
7	4.95	5.92	6.54	7.01	7.37	7.68	7.94	8.17	8.37
8	4.75	5.64	6.20	6.62	6.96	7.24	7.47	7.68	7.86
9	4.60	5.43	5.96	6.35	6.66	6.91	7.13	7.33	7.49
10	4.48	5.27	5.77	6.14	6.43	6.67	6.87	7.05	7.21
11	4.39	5.15	5.62	5.97	6.25	6.48	6.67	6.84	6.99
12	4.32	5.05	5.50	5.84	6.10	6.32	6.51	6.67	6.81
13	4.26	4.96	5.40	5.73	5.98	6.19	6.37	6.53	6.67
14	4.21	4.89	5.32	5.63	5.88	6.08	6.26	6.41	6.54
15	4.17	4.84	5.25	5.56	5.80	5.99	6.16	6.31	6.44
16	4.13	4.79	5.19	5.49	5.72	5.92	6.08	6.22	6.35
17	4.10	4.74	5.14	5.43	5.66	5.85	6.01	6.15	6.27
18	4.07	4.70	5.09	5.38	5.60	5.79	5.94	6.08	6.20
19	4.05	4.67	5.05	5.33	5.55	5.73	5.89	6.02	6.14
20	4.02	4.64	5.02	5.29	5.51	5.69	5.84	5.97	6.09
24	3.96	4.55	4.91	5.17	5.37	5.54	5.69	5.81	5.92
30	3.89	4.45	4.89	5.05	5.24	5.40	5.54	5.65	5.76
40	3.82	4.37	4.70	4.93	5.11	5.26	5.39	5.50	5.60
60	3.76	4.28	4.59	4.82	4.99	5.13	5.25	5.36	5.45
120	3.70	4.20	4.50	4.71	4.87	5.01	5.12	5.21	5.30
∞	3.64	4.12	4.40	4.60	4.76	4.88	4.99	5.08	5.16

Source: From Pearson, E. S., and Hartley, H. O., editors;
Biometrika Tables for Statisticians, ed. 3, vol. I. Cambridge:
Cambridge Univ. Press, 1966, with the kind permission
of the trustees and publishers.

Table 78   Tukey Test (continued)

$(p = 0.01)$

$n =$ the total number of means being compared

$v =$ degrees of freedom of denominator of F test

v＼n	11	12	13	14	15	16	17	18	19	20
1	253.2	260.0	266.2	271.8	277.0	281.8	286.3	290.4	294.3	298.0
2	32.59	33.40	34.13	34.81	35.43	36.00	36.53	37.03	37.50	37.95
3	17.13	17.53	17.89	18.22	18.52	18.81	19.07	19.32	19.55	19.77
4	12.57	12.84	13.09	13.32	13.53	13.73	13.91	14.08	14.24	14.40
5	10.48	10.70	10.89	11.08	11.24	11.40	11.55	11.68	11.81	11.93
6	9.30	9.48	9.65	9.81	9.95	10.08	10.21	10.32	10.43	10.54
7	8.55	8.71	8.86	9.00	9.12	9.24	9.35	9.46	9.55	9.65
8	8.03	8.18	8.31	8.44	8.55	8.66	8.76	8.85	8.94	9.03
9	7.65	7.78	7.91	8.03	8.13	8.23	8.33	8.41	8.49	8.57
10	7.36	7.49	7.60	7.71	7.81	7.91	7.99	8.08	8.15	8.23
11	7.13	7.25	7.36	7.46	7.56	7.65	7.73	7.81	7.88	7.95
12	6.94	7.06	7.17	7.26	7.36	7.44	7.52	7.59	7.66	7.73
13	6.79	6.90	7.01	7.10	7.19	7.27	7.35	7.42	7.48	7.55
14	6.66	6.77	6.87	6.96	7.05	7.13	7.20	7.27	7.33	7.39
15	6.55	6.66	6.76	6.84	6.93	7.00	7.07	7.14	7.20	7.26
16	6.46	6.56	6.66	6.74	6.82	6.90	6.97	7.03	7.09	7.15
17	6.38	6.48	6.57	6.66	6.73	6.81	6.87	6.94	7.00	7.05
18	6.31	6.41	6.50	6.58	6.65	6.73	6.79	6.85	6.91	6.97
19	6.25	6.34	6.43	6.51	6.58	6.65	6.72	6.78	6.84	6.89
20	6.19	6.28	6.37	6.45	6.52	6.59	6.65	6.71	6.77	6.82
24	6.02	6.11	6.19	6.26	6.33	6.39	6.45	6.51	6.56	6.61
30	5.85	5.93	6.01	6.08	6.14	6.20	6.26	6.31	6.36	6.41
40	5.69	5.76	5.83	5.90	5.96	6.02	6.07	6.12	6.16	6.21
60	5.53	5.60	5.67	5.73	5.78	5.84	5.89	5.93	5.97	6.01
120	5.37	5.44	5.50	5.56	5.61	5.66	5.71	5.75	5.79	5.83
∞	5.23	5.29	5.35	5.40	5.45	5.49	5.54	5.57	5.61	5.65

Statistics for Education and Physical Education

Example 2   Using the Kruskal-Wallis One-Way Analysis of Variance by Ranks

Eighteen children's paintings on a theme entitled 'Disaster' are judged for originality and their rank order of merit is classified according to the secondary school stream in which the children are placed for their academic work.

We wish to find out whether or not the originality of the children's paintings is associated with their placement in streams for other school work. In other words, with respect to the data in Table 79 below, are the four samples A, B, C, and D all drawn from the same population? The null hypothesis (H_0) in this case is that there is no association between originality of paintings and stream placement.

Table 79   Rank Order of Merit of Children's Paintings

Secondary school stream			
A	B	C	D
2	1	6	8
3	4	9	15
5	7	12	16
10	11	14	17
13			18

The Kruskal-Wallis One-Way Analysis of Variance by Ranks is appropriate to our problem. The assumptions we make in using this test are that the populations from which our samples are drawn have similar distributions, that our samples are drawn at random and that they are independent of each other.

H, the statistic used in the Kruskal-Wallis Test, is given by the formula:

$$H = \frac{12K}{N(N + 1)} - 3(N + 1)$$

where N = the number of cases in all the samples combined

and K = the total of the squared sum of the ranks in each of the samples divided by the respective number of cases in each of the samples. That is, where R_A, R_B, R_C, and R_D are the sum of the ranks for each of our samples and n_A, n_B, n_C, n_D are the number of cases in each of the samples, then:

$$K = \frac{R_A^2}{n_A} + \frac{R_B^2}{n_B} + \frac{R_C^2}{n_C} + \frac{R_D^2}{n_D}$$

Below we have set out our data and computed R and n for each of our four samples.

212

Table 80 Sum of the Ranks in the Four Samples of Paintings by Secondary School Streams

A	B	C	D
2	1	6	8
3	4	9	15
5	7	12	16
10	11	14	17
13			18
$R_A = 33$	$R_B = 23$	$R_C = 41$	$R_D = 74$
$n_A = 5$	$n_B = 4$	$n_C = 4$	$n_D = 5$

PROCEDURE IN CALCULATING H

1 Rank all the cases irrespective of stream designation from 1 to 18.

2 Sum the ranks for each sample R_A, R_B, R_C, R_D.

3 Compute K.

In our example:

$$K = \frac{R_A^2}{n_A} + \frac{R_B^2}{n_B} + \frac{R_C^2}{n_C} + \frac{R_D^2}{n_D} = \frac{(33)^2}{5} + \frac{(23)^2}{4} + \frac{(41)^2}{4} + \frac{(74)^2}{5} = 1865.5$$

Substituting into our formula:

$$H = \frac{12(1865.5)}{18(18 + 1)} - 3(18 + 1) = \frac{22386}{342} - 57$$

$$H = 8.46$$

Where there are more than five cases in each of the samples or, as in our case, there are more than three samples, the significance of H is obtained from the chi square table (Appendix 2).

Degrees of freedom are given by the formula:

d.f. $= k - 1$ where k is the number of samples

In the present example d.f. $= 4 - 1 = 3$.

From the chi square table in Appendix 2 we see that a value of 7.81 (d.f. $= 3$) is required for H to be significant at $p = 0.05$. Our obtained value of 8.46 exceeds this. We therefore reject the null hypothesis and conclude that the samples cannot be assumed to have been drawn from the same population. Put differently, there appears to be an association between the judgement of originality in the children's paintings and their placement in academic streams for other aspects of their school work.

213

THE SIGNIFICANCE OF *H* FOR SMALL SAMPLES

Where the researcher is comparing rank ordering in three samples and the number of cases in each of the samples does not exceed five, the significance of *H* may be obtained by reference to Table 81 below.

The power efficiency of the Kruskal-Wallis test relative to the parametric *F*-test is reported as 95.5% (Gibbons 1976).

Table 81   Probabilities Associated with Values as Large as Observed Values of *H* in the Kruskal-Wallis One Way Analysis of Variance by Ranks

k = 3			k = 3			k = 4			k = 4		
Sample sizes	0.05	0.01	Sample sizes	0.05	0.01	Sample sizes	0.05	0.01	Sample sizes	0.05	0.01
2 2 2	—	—	5 5 3	5.705	7.578	2 2 1 1	—	—	4 4 4 1	6.725	8.588
3 2 1	—	—	5 5 4	5.666	7.823	2 2 2 1	5.679	—	4 4 4 2	6.957	8.871
3 2 2	4.714	—	5 5 5	5.780	8.000	2 2 2 2	6.167	6.667	4 4 4 3	7.142	9.075
3 3 1	5.143	—	6 1 1	—	—	3 1 1 1	—	—	4 4 4 4	7.235	9.287
3 3 2	5.361	—	6 2 1	4.822	—	3 2 1 1	—	—			
3 3 3	5.600	7.200	6 2 2	5.345	6.655	3 2 2 1	5.833	—	k = 5		
4 2 1	—	—	6 3 1	4.855	6.873	3 2 2 2	6.333	7.133			
4 2 2	5.333	—	6 3 2	5.348	6.970	3 3 1 1	6.333	—	Sample sizes	0.05	0.01
4 3 1	5.208	—	6 3 3	5.615	7.410	3 3 2 1	6.244	7.200			
4 3 2	5.444	6.444	6 4 1	4.947	7.106	3 3 2 2	6.527	7.636	2 2 1 1 1	—	—
4 3 3	5.791	6.745	6 4 2	5.340	7.340	3 3 3 1	6.600	7.400	2 2 2 1 1	6.750	—
4 4 1	4.967	6.667	6 4 3	5.610	7.500	3 3 3 2	6.727	8.015	2 2 2 2 1	7.133	7.533
4 4 2	5.455	7.036	6 4 4	5.681	7.795	3 3 3 3	7.000	8.538	2 2 2 2 2	7.418	8.291
4 4 3	5.598	7.144	6 5 1	4.990	7.182	4 1 1 1	—	—	3 1 1 1 1	—	—
4 4 4	5.692	7.654	6 5 2	5.338	7.376	4 2 1 1	5.833	—	3 2 1 1 1	6.583	—
5 2 1	5.000	—	6 5 3	5.602	7.590	4 2 2 1	6.133	7.000	3 2 2 1 1	6.800	7.600
5 2 2	5.160	6.533	6 5 4	5.661	7.936	4 2 2 2	6.545	7.391	3 2 2 2 1	7.309	8.127
5 3 1	4.960	—	6 5 5	5.729	8.028	4 3 1 1	6.178	7.067	3 2 2 2 2	7.682	8.682
5 3 2	5.251	6.909	6 6 1	4.945	7.121	4 3 2 1	6.309	7.455	3 3 1 1 1	7.111	—
5 3 3	5.648	7.079	6 6 2	5.410	7.467	4 3 2 2	6.621	7.871	3 3 2 1 1	7.200	8.073
5 4 1	4.985	6.955	6 6 3	5.625	7.725	4 3 3 1	6.545	7.758	3 3 2 2 1	7.591	8.576
5 4 2	5.273	7.205	6 6 4	5.724	8.000	4 3 3 2	6.795	8.333	3 3 2 2 2	7.910	9.115
5 4 3	5.656	7.445	6 6 5	5.765	8.124	4 3 3 3	6.984	8.659	3 3 3 1 1	7.576	8.424
5 4 4	5.657	7.760	6 6 6	5.801	8.222	4 4 1 1	5.945	7.909	3 3 3 2 1	7.769	9.051
5 5 1	5.127	7.309	7 7 7	5.819	8.378	4 4 2 1	6.386	7.909	3 3 3 2 2	8.044	9.505
5 5 2	5.338	7.338	8 8 8	5.805	8.465	4 4 2 2	6.731	8.346	3 3 3 3 1	8.000	9.451
						4 4 3 1	6.635	8.231	3 3 3 3 2	8.200	9.876
						4 4 3 2	6.874	8.621	3 3 3 3 3	8.333	10.20
						4 4 3 3	7.038	8.876			

Source: Table 4.2, Neave, H. R.; *Statistics Tables*, London: George Allen & Unwin, 1978, p. 49, with the kind permission of the author and publisher.

10.9 Factorial Designs – The Effect of Two or More Independent Variables on the Dependent Variable
(a) No Repeated Measures on Factors

		Independent variable A (Factor A)	
		Level A_1	Level A_2
Independent variable B (Factor B)	Level B_1	Group 1 $\quad X_A$ subjects $\quad X_B$ A, B, C $\quad X_C$	Group 3 $\quad X_G$ subjects $\quad X_H$ G, H, J $\quad X_J$
	Level B_2	Group 2 $\quad X_D$ subjects $\quad X_E$ D, E, F $\quad X_F$	Group 4 $\quad X_K$ subjects $\quad X_L$ K, L, M $\quad X_M$

Example 1   Using Two-Way Analysis of Variance – Single Observations on Separate Groups (Fixed Effects, Completely Randomized Model)

Two-way analysis of variance techniques are used to estimate the effect of *two* independent variables (factors) on a dependent variable. The hypothetical data presented in Table 82 allow us to illustrate the use of a two-way technique for single observations on separate groups.

The reader is advised to refer to page 161 for a brief explanation of the rationale behind analysis of variance techniques before proceeding to the present example.

We have purposely included only a small number of scores in each of the cells in our example in order to avoid lengthy and cumbersome calculations. It should be remembered, however, that in order to make a valid analysis, the same assumptions that govern a one-way analysis of variance have to be met.

Suppose that from a population of first year undergraduates who have followed a course in introductory statistics, we have randomly drawn samples of male and female students and have given them a statistics examination. Suppose further, that half the male and half the female students have had specific guidance in study techniques by way of preparing for the test and that the others have received no guidance.

Two-way analysis of variance allows us to answer a number of questions concerning our samples and their performances in the statistics examination. For example: Do males differ significantly from females in their test results? Does guidance in study techniques affect examination performance? Is there an interaction effect of sex and study guidance in respect of the results? In other words, do females without guidance do better than males with guidance and so on?

The null hypotheses in respect of each of the questions we have raised are that neither sex, nor study guidance nor any interaction of these two factors affects examination performance. Our data are set out in Table 82.

The total variance in this single observation design can be partitioned into:

SYSTEMATIC EFFECTS

1 BETWEEN GROUPS (treatments or conditions) variance is the variance between means caused by the independent variables. These effects can be separated as follows:

(a)   FACTOR A – the effect of study guidance techniques on the variance.

(b)   FACTOR B – the effect of sex on the variance.

(c)   INTERACTION A × B – the combined effects of study guidance and sex on the variance.

Table 82   Examination Results in Elementary Statistics

		Independent variable A (Factor A)	
		Guidance in study	No guidance in study
Independent variable B (Factor B)	Female students	(Group 1) 18 16 18	(Group 2) 8 10 7
	Male students	(Group 3) 24 25 21	(Group 4) 18 20 21

ERROR EFFECTS

2   WITHIN GROUPS (CELLS) variance is the variance due to subject differences and uncontrolled factors.

PROCEDURES FOR COMPUTING TWO-WAY ANALYSIS OF VARIANCE (SINGLE OBSERVATIONS ON SEPARATE GROUPS)

1   Square each score (X^2) and total both the scores $(\sum X)$ and the squares of scores $(\sum X^2)$ for each group. Enter in separate data Table 83.

2   Compute the grand total (GT).

$$GT = \frac{(\sum X)^2}{N_T}$$

$$= \frac{(206)^2}{12} = 3536.33$$

where N_T = total number of scores.

3   Compute the TOTAL sum of squares (SS_{TOTAL}).

$$SS_{\text{TOTAL}} = \sum X^2_{\text{TOTAL}} - GT$$
$$= 3924 - 3536.33 = 387.67$$

217

Table 83   Two-Way Analysis of Variance (Single Observations, Separate Groups): Computational Procedures

| | | Factor A | | | | |
		Guidance (Column 1)		No guidance (Column 2)		Total X for rows
		X_1	X_1^2	X_2	X_2^2	
F	Female (Row 1)	18	324	8	64	26
a		16	256	10	100	26
c		18	324	7	49	25
t		52	904	25	213	77
o						
r		X_3	X_3^2	X_4	X_4^2	
B	Male (Row 2)	24	576	18	324	42
		25	625	20	400	45
		21	441	21	441	42
		70	1642	59	1165	129
	Total X for Columns	122		84		

$$\sum X_{\text{TOTAL}} = 52 + 25 + 70 + 59 = 206$$
$$\sum X_{\text{TOTAL}}^2 = 904 + 213 + 1642 + 1165 = 3924$$

4   Compute the BETWEEN GROUPS sum of squares (SS_{BETWEEN}).

$$SS_{\text{BETWEEN}} = \left[\frac{(\sum X_1)^2}{N_1} + \frac{(\sum X_2)^2}{N_2} + \frac{(\sum X_3)^2}{N_3} + \frac{(\sum X_4)^2}{N_4}\right] - GT$$

$$= \left[\frac{(52)^2}{3} + \frac{(25)^2}{3} + \frac{(70)^2}{3} + \frac{(59)^2}{3}\right] - 3536.33$$

$$= [901.33 + 208.33 + 1633.33 + 1160.33] - 3536.33$$

$$= 366.9$$

5   Compute the sum of squares for FACTOR A (SS_{FA}).

$$SS_{\text{FA}} = \frac{(\text{Sum of column 1})^2}{\text{Number in column 1}} + \frac{(\text{Sum of column 2})^2}{\text{Number in column 2}} - GT$$

$$= \frac{(122)^2}{6} + \frac{(84)^2}{6} - 3536.33$$

$$= 2480.66 + 1176 - 3536.33$$

$$= 120.33$$

6 Compute the sum of squares for FACTOR B (SS_{FB}).

$$SS_{FB} = \frac{(\text{Sum of rows})^2}{\text{Number in rows}} - GT$$

$$= \frac{(\text{Sum of female } X\text{'s})^2}{\text{Number of females}} + \frac{(\text{Sum of male } X\text{'s})^2}{\text{Number of males}} - GT$$

$$= \frac{(77)^2}{6} + \frac{(129)^2}{6} - 3536.33$$

$$= 988.16 + 2773.5 - 3536.33$$

$$= 225.33$$

7 Compute the sum of squares for INTERACTION between FACTOR A and FACTOR B ($SS_{A \times B}$).

$$SS_{A \times B} = SS_{BETWEEN} - SS_{FA} - SS_{FB}$$

$$= 366.9 - 120.33 - 225.33$$

$$= 21.24$$

8 Compute the WITHIN GROUPS (CELLS) sum of squares (SS_{WITHIN}).

$$SS_{WITHIN} = SS_{TOTAL} - SS_{BETWEEN}$$

$$= 387.67 - 366.9$$

$$= 20.77$$

9 Determine the degrees of freedom for each sum of squares..

d.f. for $SS_{TOTAL} = (n - 1) = (12 - 1) = 11$

where N = total number of scores.

d.f. for $SS_{BETWEEN} = (G - 1) = (4 - 1) = 3$

where G = number of groups.

d.f. for $SS_{FA} = (C - 1) = (2 - 1) = 1$

where C = number of columns.

d.f. for $SS_{FB} = (r - 1) = (2 - 1) = 1$

where r = number of rows.

d.f. for $SS_{A \times B} = (r - 1)(C - 1) = (2 - 1)(2 - 1) = 1$

d.f. for $SS_{WITHIN} = (N - rC) = 12 - (2)(2) = 8$

10   Estimate the variances

$$\text{Var} = \frac{\text{Sum of squares}}{\text{d.f.}}$$

$$\text{Var}_{\text{FACTOR A}} = \frac{SS_{\text{FA}}}{\text{d.f.}_{\text{FA}}} = \frac{120.33}{1} = 120.33$$

$$\text{Var}_{\text{FACTOR B}} = \frac{SS_{\text{FB}}}{\text{d.f.}_{\text{FB}}} = \frac{225.33}{1} = 225.33$$

$$\text{Var}_{\text{A} \times \text{B}} = \frac{SS_{\text{A} \times \text{B}}}{\text{d.f.}_{\text{A} \times \text{B}}} = \frac{21.24}{1} = 21.24$$

11   Compute the F values for the main effects of variance table.

$$F_{\text{FACTOR A}} = \frac{\text{Var}_{\text{FACTOR A}}}{\text{Var}_{\text{WITHIN}}} = \frac{120.33}{2.59} = 46.46$$

$$F_{\text{FACTOR B}} = \frac{\text{Var}_{\text{FACTOR B}}}{\text{Var}_{\text{WITHIN}}} = \frac{225.33}{2.59} = 87.00$$

$$F_{\text{INT}} = \frac{\text{Var}_{\text{A} \times \text{B}}}{\text{Var}_{\text{WITHIN}}} = \frac{21.24}{2.59} = 8.20$$

12   Enter results in an Analysis of Variance Table.

Table 84   Analysis of Variance Table

Source of variation	Sum of squares	d.f.	Variance	F
(Between groups)	(366.9)	(3)		
Factor A	120.33	1	$\frac{120.33}{1} = 120.33$	46.46
Factor B	225.33	1	$\frac{225.33}{1} = 225.33$	87.00
Interaction (A × B)	21.24	1	$\frac{21.24}{1} = 21.24$	8.20
Within groups	20.77	8	$\frac{20.77}{8} = 2.59$	
Total	387.67	11		

13   Refer to the table in Appendix 4 to determine the significance of the F values. Our first null hypothesis is that guidance in study (Factor A) has no effect upon examination performance.

The obtained F value for Factor A, 46.46, far exceeds the F of 11.26 in the table for 1 and 8 degrees of freedom. We therefore reject the null hypothesis and conclude that guidance in study techniques has a significant effect upon examination performance.

Our second null hypothesis is that the sex of the student (Factor B) has no effect upon test results.

Again, our obtained value of 87.00 far exceeds the F of 11.26 found in the table at the 0.01 level for 1 and 8 degrees of freedom. We therefore reject the null hypothesis and conclude that male and female students do differ in their performance in the statistics examination.

Finally, our third null hypothesis is that there is no interaction effect on the test results. That is to say, the combined effects of the sex of the student and guidance or no guidance over study matters do not relate to examination performance.

The obtained value of $F = 8.20$ for interaction (A × B) exceeds the value of 5.32 found in the table at the 0.05 level for 1 and 8 degrees of freedom. We therefore reject the null hypothesis and conclude that the combined effects of the sex of the student and guidance or no guidance over study matters significantly affect the examination results.

Since the F test has shown that there are significant differences between means, we must now use the Tukey test to compare means.

We already know that the means for study guidance and for no study guidance are significantly different. We also know that the means for male and for female groups are significantly different. There is no need to apply further tests on them.

On the other hand, although we have obtained a significant F value for interaction, we do not know how many of the interaction means (the cell means) are significantly different; all we know is that at least two of them are. The Tukey test can assist us here.

PROCEDURES IN COMPUTING THE TUKEY TEST

1   Calculate the means for each cell or group and construct a table of sample mean differences.

Table 85   Sample Mean Differences and the Tukey Test

	Comparison means	M_1	M_2	M_3	M_4
Group 1 Female/ Guidance	$M_1 = 17.33$		$M_1 - M_2 = 9^*$	$M_1 - M_3 = -6^*$	$M_1 - M_4 = -2.33$
Group 2 Female/No guidance	$M_2 = 8.33$			$M_2 - M_3 = -15^*$	$M_2 - M_4 = -11.33^*$
Group 3 Male/ Guidance	$M_3 = 23.33$				$M_3 - M_4 = 3.67$
Group 4 Male/No guidance	$M_4 = 19.66$				

*   Significant difference at the 0.05 level.

2   Compute T

$$T = (q) \sqrt{\frac{\text{Var}_{\text{WITHIN}}}{N}} \quad \text{(i.e. Error Variation)}$$

where N = number in each group or the number of scores from which each mean is calculated.

The q value in the above formula is found by consulting Tables 77 and 78 and determining the value corresponding to the number of means (n in the Tukey table) and the degrees of freedom for the denominator of our prior F test. That denominator is, of course, the within groups variance and its appropriate degrees of freedom are read as r in the Tukey table.

We see that in our example, q at the 0.05 level = 4.53 when $n = 4$ and $r = 8$. Thus:

$$T_{0.05} = 4.53 \sqrt{\frac{2.59}{3}} = 4.21$$

If the T value of 4.21 is smaller than the difference between two means, then the means are significantly different. Referring to our table of mean differences we can draw the following conclusions:

(a) Female students with study guidance score significantly higher than female students who have no study guidance.

(b) Male students with study guidance score significantly higher than female students with study guidance.

(c) Male students with no study guidance score significantly higher than female students with no study guidance.

(d) Male students with study guidance score significantly higher than male students with no study guidance.

10.10　Factorial Designs – The Effect of Two or More Independent Variables on the Dependent Variable

(b)　Repeated Measures on ONE Factor

		Independent Variable A (Factor A)	
		Level A_1	Level A_2
Independent variable B (Factor B)	Level B_1	Group$_1$　X_{A_1} X_{B_1} X_{C_1}	Group$_1$　X_{A_2} X_{B_2} X_{C_2}
	Level B_2	Group$_2$　X_{E_1} X_{F_1} X_{G_1}	Group$_2$　X_{E_2} X_{F_2} X_{G_2}

Example 1   Using Two-Way Analysis of Variance–Repeated Observations on One Factor

When we wish to determine the effects of two independent variables on a dependent variable and the experimental design involves repeated measures of the same subjects on one of the independent variables, then the two-way analysis of variance we outlined on pages 216 to 220 becomes inappropriate. The following example shows the changes that have to be made as a result of different partitioning of the total variance.

Suppose that two groups of students, one containing skilled performers and the other containing unskilled performers, are selected at random and tested on a particular skills test on two separate occasions. On one occasion an audience is present and on the other no audience is present. In order to control the practice effects, half the students from each group perform in front of the audience on the first occasion and the other half perform in front of the audience on the second occasion.

By applying a two-way analysis of variance we can answer the following questions:

Do the skilled performers score higher than the unskilled performers on this particular skills test? Does performing in front of an audience have an effect on skill test scores? Is there a difference in skill test scores due to the combined effects (interaction) of skill level and audience/no audience?

Our null hypotheses in connection with these questions are that neither skilled nor unskilled performance, nor performance in front of or without an audience, nor yet any combined effects of the 'skill' or 'audience' factors, affects skill test results.

Our data are set out in Table 86 below.

Table 86 Skill Test Results

		Independent variable A (Factor A)	
		Audience (Column 1)	No audience (Column 2)
	Group 1	25	25
		21	24
		26	27
		24	26
Independent	Skilled	26	25
variable B	performers	20	19
	(Row 1)	19	22
		22	21
		20	19
		23	23
(Factor B)	Group 2	12	14
		14	14
		12	15
		9	12
	Unskilled	15	15
	performers	13	13
	(Row 2)	12	16
		11	14
		15	15
		13	16

The assumptions governing the two-way analysis of variance (repeated observations on one factor) are similar to those for the one-way analysis of variance detailed on page 161.

In this repeated measure design, the total variance can be partitioned as follows:

SYSTEMATIC EFFECTS

1 The variance caused by the main effects of the independent variables, namely:

(a) FACTOR A – The effects of audience or no audience on the variance.

(b) FACTOR B – The effects of skill or non-skill level on the variance.

(c) INTERACTION A × B – The combined effects of factors A and B on the variance.

ERROR EFFECTS

2 BETWEEN SUBJECTS ERROR (WITHIN GROUPS) variance due to subject differences and uncontrolled factors.

3 WITHIN SUBJECTS ERROR variance caused by individual variations on the two testing situations.

PROCEDURES FOR COMPUTING TWO-WAY ANALYSIS OF VARIANCE (REPEATED MEASURES ON ONE FACTOR)

1 Square each score (X^2) and total the scores $(\sum X)$ and the squares of scores $(\sum X^2)$ for each cell. Enter these in separate data table.

2 Compute the Grand Total (GT).

$$GT = \frac{(\sum X)^2}{N_T}$$

$$= \frac{(727)^2}{40} = 13{,}213.22$$

where N_T = total number of scores.

3 Compute the TOTAL sum of squares (SS_{TOTAL}).

$$SS_{\text{TOTAL}} = \sum X^2_{\text{TOTAL}} - GT$$
$$= 14281 - 13213.22 = 1067.78$$

4 Compute the sum of squares for FACTOR A (SS_{FA}).

$$SS_{FA} = \frac{(\text{Sum of column 1})^2}{\text{Number in column 1}} + \frac{(\text{Sum of column 2})^2}{\text{Number in column 2}} - GT$$

$$= \frac{(352)^2}{20} + \frac{(375)^2}{20} - 13213.22$$

$$= \frac{123904}{20} + \frac{140625}{20} - 13213.22$$

$$= 6195.2 + 7031.25 - 13213.22$$

$$= 13.23$$

227

Statistics for Education and Physical Education

Table 87 Skill Test Results: Computational Procedures for Analysis of Variance

		Factor A			Totals for subjects	(Totals)² for subjects
	Subjects	Audience		No audience		
	Group 1	X_1	X_1^2	X_2 X_2^2	$(X_1 + X_2)$	$(X_1 + X_2)^2$
		25	625	25 625	50	2500
		21	441	24 576	45	2025
		26	676	27 729	53	2809
		24	576	26 676	50	2500
		26	676	25 625	51	2601
	Skilled	20	400	19 361	39	1521
F		19	361	22 484	41	1681
a		22	484	21 441	43	1849
c		20	400	19 361	39	1521
t		23	529	23 529	46	2116
o		226	5168	231 5407	457	21123
r	Group 2	X_3	X_3^2	X_4 X_4^2	$(X_3 + X_4)$	$(X_3 + X_4)^2$
B		12	144	14 196	26	676
		14	196	14 196	28	784
		12	144	15 225	27	729
		9	81	12 144	21	441
		15	225	15 225	30	900
	Unskilled	13	169	13 169	26	676
		12	144	16 256	28	784
		11	121	14 196	25	625
		15	225	15 225	30	900
		13	169	16 256	29	841
		126	1618	144 2088	270	7356
	Column total	352	6786	375 7495		

$$\sum X_{\text{TOTAL}} = 226 + 231 + 126 + 144 = 727$$
$$\sum X_{\text{TOTAL}}^2 = 5168 + 5407 + 1618 + 2088 = 14281$$

5 Compute the sum of squares for FACTOR B (SS_{FB}).

$$SS_{FB} = \frac{(\text{Sum of rows})^2}{\text{Number in rows}} - GT$$

$$= \frac{(\text{Sum of skilled } X\text{'s})^2}{\text{Number of skilled scores}} + \frac{(\text{Sum of unskilled } X\text{'s})^2}{\text{Number of unskilled scores}} - GT$$

$$= \frac{(457)^2}{20} + \frac{(270)^2}{20} - 13213.22$$

$$= 10442.45 + 3645 - 13213.22$$

$$= 874.23$$

6 Compute INTERACTION sum of squares ($SS_{A \times B}$).

$$S_{A \times B} = \frac{(\sum X_1)^2}{n_1} + \frac{(\sum X_2)^2}{n_2} + \frac{(\sum X_3)^2}{n_3} + \frac{(\sum X_4)^2}{n_4} - SS_{FA} - SS_{FB} - GT$$

$$= \frac{(226)^2}{10} + \frac{(231)^2}{10} + \frac{(126)^2}{10} + \frac{(144)^2}{10} - 13.23 - 874.23 - 13213.22$$

$$= 5107.6 + 5336.1 + 1587.6 + 2073.6 - 13.23 - 874.23 - 13213.22$$

$$= 4.22$$

where n = number in cell.

7 Compute BETWEEN SUBJECTS ERROR sum of squares (SS_{BSE}).

$$SS_{BSE} = \frac{\sum (X_1 + X_2)^2 + (X_3 + X_4)^2}{\text{Number of columns}} - SS_{FB} - GT$$

$$= \frac{21123 + 7356}{2} - 874.23 - 13213.22$$

$$= 14239.5 - 874.23 - 13213.22$$

$$= 152.05$$

8 Compute WITHIN SUBJECTS ERROR sum of squares (SS_{WSE}).

$$SS_{WSE} = SS_{TOTAL} - SS_{FA} - SS_{FB} - SS_{A \times B} - SS_{BSE}$$

$$= 1067.78 - 13.23 - 874.23 - 4.22 - 152.05$$

$$= 24.05$$

9 Determine the degrees of freedom for each of the sum of squares.

d.f. for $SS_{TOTAL} = (N - 1) = (40 - 1) = 39$

where N = total number of scores.

d.f. for $SS_{FA} = (C - 1) = (2 - 1) = 1$

where C = number of columns.

d.f. for $SS_{FB} = (r - 1) = (2 - 1) = 1$

where r = number of rows.

d.f. for $SS_{A \times B} = (r - 1)(C - 1) = (2 - 1)(2 - 1) = 1$

d.f. for $SS_{BSE} = r(n - 1) = 2(10 - 1) = 18$

where n = number of subjects in each group.

d.f. for $SS_{WSE} = r(n - 1)(C - 1) = 2(10 - 1)(2 - 1) = 18$

10 Compute the variances for the main and error effects.

$$Var_{FACTOR\ A} = \frac{SS_{FA}}{d.f._{FA}} = \frac{13.23}{1} = 13.23$$

$$Var_{FACTOR\ B} = \frac{SS_{FB}}{d.f._{FB}} = \frac{874.23}{1} = 874.23$$

$$Var_{INT\ A \times B} = \frac{SS_{A \times B}}{d.f._{A \times B}} = \frac{4.22}{1} = 4.22$$

$$Var_{BSE} = \frac{SS_{BSE}}{d.f._{BSE}} = \frac{152.05}{18} = 8.45$$

$$Var_{WSE} = \frac{SS_{WSE}}{d.f._{WSE}} = \frac{24.05}{18} = 1.34$$

11 Compute F values for *main* effects.

$$F_{FA} = \frac{Var_{FA}}{Var_{WSE}} = \frac{13.23}{1.34} = 9.87$$

$$F_{FB} = \frac{Var_{FB}}{Var_{BSE}} = \frac{874.23}{8.45} = 103.46$$

$$F_{A \times B} = \frac{Var_{A \times B}}{Var_{WSE}} = \frac{4.22}{1.34} = 3.15$$

12   Enter the results in an Analysis of Variance Table.

Table 88   Analysis of Variance Table

Source of variation	Sum of squares	d.f.	Variance	F
Factor A	13.23	1	$\dfrac{13.23}{1} = 13.23$	9.87
Factor B	874.23	1	$\dfrac{874.23}{1} = 874.23$	103.46
Interaction A × B	4.22	1	$\dfrac{4.22}{1} = 4.22$	3.15
Within subjects error	24.05	18	$\dfrac{24.05}{18} = 1.34$	
Between subjects error	152.05	18	$\dfrac{152.05}{18} = 8.45$	
Total	1067.78	39		

Consult the table in Appendix 4 to determine the significance of the F values. Our obtained value for Factor A, $F = 9.87$ exceeds the F of 8.29 in the table at the 0.01 level for d.f. = 1, 18. We therefore reject the null hypothesis and conclude that the presence of an audience does have an effect upon students' performance in the skills test.

Similarly, our obtained value for Factor B, $F = 103.46$ far exceeds the F value of 8.29 at the 0.01 level. Again we reject the null hypothesis and conclude that skill level has an effect upon skills performance in the test situation.

Our obtained value for the Interaction A × B, $F = 3.15$ is less than the 4.41 value in the table at the 0.05 level. We therefore accept the null hypothesis and conclude that the combined effects of skill level and audience/no audience do not affect skill test performance scores.

10.11 Factorial Designs – The Effect of Two or More Independent Variables on the Dependent Variable
(c) Repeated Measures on BOTH Factors

		Independent variable A (Factor A)	
		Level A_1	Level A_2
Independent variable B	Level B_1	Group 1	Group 1
(Factor B)	Level B_2	Group 1	Group 1

OR

Group 1 subjects	Independent variable A (Factor A)			
	Level A_1		Level A_2	
	Independent variable B (Factor B)			
	Level B_1	Level B_2	Level B_1	Level B_2
M	$X_M(A_1B_1)$	$X_M(A_1B_2)$	$X_M(A_2B_1)$	$X_M(A_2B_2)$
N	$X_N(A_1B_1)$	$X_N(A_1B_2)$	$X_N(A_2B_1)$	$X_N(A_2B_2)$
O	$X_O(A_1B_1)$	$X_O(A_1B_2)$	$X_O(A_2B_1)$	$X_O(A_2B_2)$
P	$X_P(A_1B_1)$	$X_P(A_1B_2)$	$X_P(A_2B_1)$	$X_P(A_2B_2)$
Q	$X_Q(A_1B_1)$	$X_Q(A_1B_2)$	$X_Q(A_2B_1)$	$X_Q(A_2B_2)$
R	$X_R(A_1B_1)$	$X_R(A_1B_2)$	$X_R(A_2B_1)$	$X_R(A_2B_2)$

Example 1 Using the Two-Way Analysis of Variance-Repeated Observations on Both Factors

If we wish to determine the effects of *two* independent variables on a dependent variable and only one random sample is selected, the two-way analysis of variance illustrated below is appropriate. It involves the analysis of repeated measures of the same subjects on *both* independent variables.

In order to ease the computational burden in the example, we use hypothetical scores and a small sample. The reader should remember, however, that with authentic data the same assumptions apply to this analysis of variance technique as to those that have been described in earlier sections.

In an experiment to assess the effect of body position on recovery rate after exercise, a random sample of physical education students was drawn and their recovery rates monitored while sitting, standing, and lying after standardized periods of both heavy and light exercise.

We wish to answer the following questions:

1 *Is recovery rate after exercise related to the position adopted during the recovery period?*

2 *Does the recovery rate depend upon the type of exercise undertaken?*

3 *Is there a combined effect of body position and type of exercise on the recovery rates?*

Our hypothetical data are set out in Table 89 below.

Table 89   Recovery Rates After Exercise: Format A

		Independent variable (P)		
		Sitting (P_1)	Standing (P_2)	Lying (P_3)
I n d e p e n d e n t		(Group 1)	(Group 1)	(Group 1)
	Light Exercise (E_1)	3 4 3 5	4 4 4 5	3 4 3 5
V a r (E)		(Group 1)	(Group 1)	(Group 1)
	Heavy Exercise (E_2)	5 5 7 6	6 5 6 6	5 7 6 7

Although Table 89 includes all the relevant information needed for our analysis of variance, the form of presentation does not easily lend itself to the computational description that follows. The same information is therefore set out in a more suitable format in Table 90.

Table 90   Recovery Rates After Exercise: Format B

Subjects (s)	Light exercise (E_1)			Heavy exercise (E_2)		
	Sitting (P_1)	Standing (P_2)	Lying (P_3)	Sitting (P_1)	Standing (P_2)	Lying (P_3)
1	3	4	3	5	6	5
2	4	4	4	5	5	7
3	3	4	3	7	6	6
4	5	5	5	6	6	7

The total variance in this repeated measures design can be partitioned into:

1   BETWEEN SUBJECTS VARIANCE.

2   WITHIN SUBJECTS VARIANCE.

The within subjects variance has both systematic and error effects on the total variance. The main effects of the independent variables make up the systematic variance, whereas the error effects are caused by possible individual variations between the repeated measures. This within subjects variance can be sub-divided as follows:

SYSTEMATIC EFFECTS

(*a*)   FACTOR E – the effect of differing levels of exercise on the variance.

(*b*)   FACTOR P – the effect of different recovery positions on the variance.

(*c*)   INTERACTION E × P – the combined effects of exercise and recovery position.

ERROR EFFECTS

(*d*)   EXERCISE × SUBJECTS WITHIN GROUPS ERROR – the effect due to the same subjects under both exercise conditions.

(*e*)   POSITION × SUBJECTS WITHIN GROUPS ERROR – the effect due to the variation between repeated measures of the same subjects in each recovery position.

(*f*)   INTERACTION (E × P) × SUBJECTS WITHIN GROUPS ERROR.

PROCEDURES IN COMPUTING THE TWO-WAY ANALYSIS OF
VARIANCE – REPEATED OBSERVATIONS ON BOTH FACTORS

Table 91 below will assist the reader to interpret the various formulae used in the computations.

Table 91 Interpretation of Two-Way Analysis of Variance

Subjects	Light exercise E_1			Total	Heavy exercise E_2			Total	Subject totals
	P_1	P_2	P_3		P_1	P_2	P_3		
S_1				S_1E_1				S_1E_2	$(S_1E_1 + S_1E_2)$
S_2				S_2E_1				S_2E_2	$(S_2E_1 + S_2E_2)$
S_3				S_3E_1				S_3E_2	$(S_3E_1 + S_3E_2)$
S_4				S_4E_1				S_4E_2	$(S_4E_1 + S_4E_2)$
Column totals	C_1	C_2	C_3		C_4	C_5	C_6		
Exercise totals	$E_1 = C_1 + C_2 + C_3$				$E_2 = C_4 + C_5 + C_6$				
Position totals	$P_1 = (C_1 + C_4),$			$P_2 = (C_2 + C_5),$			$P_3 = (C_3 + C_6)$		

1 Prepare a data table including the rows and columns totals.

Table 92 Recovery Rate Results Prepared for Analysis of Variance

Subjects	Light exercise E_1			Total	Heavy exercise E_2			Total	Subject totals
	Sitting P_1	Standing P_2	Lying P_3		Sitting P_1	Standing P_2	Lying P_3		
S_1	3	4	3	10	5	6	5	16	$10 + 16 = 26$
S_2	4	4	4	12	5	5	7	17	$12 + 17 = 29$
S_3	3	4	3	10	7	6	6	19	$10 + 19 = 29$
S_4	5	5	5	15	6	6	7	19	$15 + 19 = 34$
Column totals	15	17	15		23	23	25		$\sum X = 118$
Exercise totals	$E_1 = 15 + 17 + 15 = 47$				$E_2 = 23 + 23 + 25 = 71$				
Position totals	$P_1 = (15 + 23) = 38,$			$P_2 = 17 + 23 = 40,$			$P_3 = 15 + 25 = 40$		

n = number of subjects = 4.
q = number of exercise treatments = 2.
r = number of positions = 3.

2 Square each score and total the raw scores $(\sum X)$ and squares of scores $(\sum X)^2$.

$$\sum X = 15 + 17 + 15 + 23 + 23 + 25 = 118$$
$$\sum X^2 = 3^2 + 4^2 + \cdots + 6^2 + 7^2 \quad = 618$$

3 Compute the Grand Total (GT).

$$GT = \frac{(\sum X)^2}{N_T}$$
$$= \frac{(118)^2}{24} = 580.16$$

where N_T = total number of scores.

4 Compute the TOTAL sum of squares (SS_{TOTAL}).

$$SS_{\text{TOTAL}} = \sum X^2 - GT$$
$$= 618 - 580.16 = 37.84$$

5 Compute the BETWEEN SUBJECTS sum of squares (SS_{BET}).

$$SS_{\text{BET}} = [S] - GT$$
$$= \left[\frac{(S_1)^2}{qr} + \frac{(S_2)^2}{qr} + \frac{(S_3)^2}{qr} + \frac{(S_4)^2}{qr} \right] - GT$$
$$= \left[\frac{(26)^2 + (29)^2 + (29)^2 + (34)^2}{(2)(3)} \right] - 580.16$$
$$= [585.66] - 580.16 = 5.5$$

6 Compute the sum of squares for EXERCISE (SS_{EX}).

$$SS_{\text{EX}} = [E] - GT$$
$$= \left[\frac{E_1^2}{rn} + \frac{E_2^2}{rn} \right] - GT$$
$$= \left[\frac{47^2}{(3)(4)} + \frac{71^2}{(3)(4)} \right] - 580.16$$
$$= [604.16] - 580.16 = 24.00$$

7 Compute the sum of squares for POSITIONS (SS_{POSN}).

$$SS_{POSN} = [P] - GT$$

$$= \left[\frac{P_1^2}{qn} + \frac{P_2^2}{qn} + \frac{P_3^2}{qn}\right] - GT$$

$$= \left[\frac{(38)^2}{(2)(4)} + \frac{(40)^2}{(2)(4)} + \frac{(40)^2}{(2)(4)}\right] - 580.16$$

$$= [180.5 + 200 + 200] - 580.16$$

$$= [580.5] - 580.16 = 0.33$$

8 Compute the INTERACTION sum of squares ($SS_{EX \times POSN}$).

$$SS_{EX \times POSN} = [EP] - E - P + GT$$

$$= \left[\frac{C_1^2}{n} + \frac{C_2^2}{n} + \frac{C_3^2}{n} + \frac{C_4^2}{n} + \frac{C_5^2}{n} + \frac{C_6^2}{n}\right] - E - P + GT$$

$$= \left[\frac{(15)^2}{4} + \frac{(17)^2}{4} + \frac{(15)^2}{4} + \frac{(23)^2}{4} + \frac{(23)^2}{4} + \frac{(25)^2}{4}\right]$$

$$- 604.16 - 580.5 + 580.16$$

$$= [605.5] - 604.16 - 580.5 + 580.16 = 1.00$$

9 Compute the EXERCISE × SUBJECTS ERROR sum of squares ($SS_{EX \times SUBJ}$).

$$SS_{EX \times SUBJ} = [ES] - E - S + GT$$

$$= \left[\frac{(S_1 E_1)^2}{r} + \frac{(S_1 E_2)^2}{r} + \frac{(S_2 E_1)^2}{r} + \cdots + \frac{(S_4 E_2)^2}{r}\right] - E - S + GT$$

$$= \left[\frac{(10)^2}{3} + \frac{(16)^2}{3} + \frac{(12)^2}{3} + \frac{(17)^2}{3} + \frac{(10)^2}{3} + \frac{(19)^2}{3} + \frac{(15)^2}{3} + \frac{(19)^2}{3}\right]$$

$$- 604.16 - 585.66 + 580.16$$

$$= [612] - 604.16 - 585.66 + 580.16 = 2.33$$

10 Compute the POSITION × SUBJECTS ERROR sum of squares ($SS_{POSN \times SUBJ}$).

$$SS_{POSN \times SUBJ} = [PS] - P - S + GT$$

$$= \left[\frac{\sum (\text{Subjects' scores in each position})^2}{q}\right] - P - S + GT$$

$$= \left[\frac{(3+5)^2}{2} + \frac{(4+6)^2}{2} + \frac{(3+5)^2}{2} + \cdots + \frac{(5+6)^2}{2} + \frac{(5+7)^2}{2}\right]$$

$$- 580.5 - 585.66 + 580.16$$

$$= [589] - 580.5 - 585.66 + 580.16 = 3.00$$

11 Compute the INTERACTION × SUBJECTS ERROR sum of squares $(SS_{(EX \times POSN)SUBJ})$.

$$SS_{(EX \times POSN)SUBJ} = \sum X^2 - EP - PS - ES + E + P + S - GT$$
$$= 618 - 605.5 - 589 - 612 + 604.16$$
$$+ 580.5 + 585.66 - 580.16$$
$$= 1.66$$

12 Determine the degrees of freedom for the main and error effects.

d.f. for $SS_{TOTAL} = (N - 1) = (24 - 1) = 23$

d.f. for $SS_{BET} = (n - 1) = (4 - 1) = 3$

d.f. for $SS_{EX} = (q - 1) = (2 - 1) = 1$

d.f. for $SS_{POSN} = (r - 1) = (3 - 1) = 2$

d.f. for $SS_{EX \times POSN} = (r - 1)(q - 1) = (2 - 1)(3 - 1) = 2$

d.f. for $SS_{EX \times SUBJ} = (q - 1)(n - 1) = (2 - 1)(4 - 1) = 3$

d.f. for $SS_{POSN \times SUBJ} = (r - 1)(n - 1) = (3 - 1)(4 - 1) = 6$

d.f. for $SS_{(P \times E)SUBJ} = (n - 1)(q - 1)(r - 1) = (4 - 1)(2 - 1)(3 - 1) = 6$

13 Compute variances for main and error effects.

$$Var_{EX} = \frac{SS_{EX}}{d.f._{EX}} = \frac{24.00}{1} = 24.00$$

$$Var_{POSN} = \frac{SS_{POSN}}{d.f._{POSN}} = \frac{0.33}{2} = 0.17$$

$$Var_{EX \times POSN} = \frac{SS_{EX \times POSN}}{d.f._{EX \times POSN}} = \frac{1.00}{2} = 0.50$$

$$Var_{EX \times SUBJ} = \frac{SS_{EX \times SUBJ}}{d.f._{EX \times SUBJ}} = \frac{2.33}{3} = 0.78$$

$$Var_{POSN \times SUBJ} = \frac{SS_{POSN \times SUBJ}}{d.f._{POSN \times SUBJ}} = \frac{3.00}{6} = 0.5$$

$$Var_{(E \times P)SUBJ} = \frac{SS_{(EX \times POSN)SUBJ}}{d.f._{(EX \times POSN)SUBJ}} = \frac{1.66}{6} = 0.28$$

14   Compute F for main effects.

$$F_{EX} = \frac{Var_{EX}}{Var_{EX \times SUBJ}} = \frac{24.00}{0.78} = 30.77$$

$$F_{POSN} = \frac{Var_{POSN}}{Var_{POSN \times SUBJ}} = \frac{0.17}{0.5} = 0.33$$

$$F_{POSN \times EX} = \frac{Var_{EX \times POSN}}{Var_{(E \times P)SUBJ}} = \frac{0.50}{0.28} = 1.79$$

15   Enter the results in an analysis of variance table.

Table 93   Analysis of Variance Table

Source of variation	Sum of squares	d.f.	Variance	F
Between subjects	5.5	3		
(Within subjects)	(32.33)	(20)		
Exercise	24.00	1	$\frac{24.00}{1} = 24.00$	$\frac{24.00}{0.78} = 30.77$
Position	0.33	2	$\frac{0.33}{2} = 0.17$	$\frac{0.17}{0.5} = 0.33$
Ex. × Posn.	1.00	2	$\frac{1.00}{2} = 0.50$	$\frac{0.50}{0.28} = 1.79$
Ex. × Subj. Error	2.33	3	$\frac{2.33}{3} = 0.78$	
Posn. × Subj. Error	3.0	6	$\frac{3.00}{6} = 0.5$	
(Ex. × Posn.) Subj. Error	1.66	6	$\frac{1.66}{6} = 0.28$	

Consult the table in Appendix 4 to determine the significance of the F values. The obtained value for the exercise effect, $F = 30.77$ exceeds the F value of 18.51 in the table at the 0.05 level for d.f. 1 and 2. We therefore reject the null hypothesis and conclude that type of exercise does affect recovery rate.

The obtained value for the recovery position effect, $F = 0.33$, does not exceed the F value of 5.14 in the table at the 0.05 level for d.f. 2 and 6. We therefore accept the null hypothesis and conclude that recovery position does not affect recovery rate.

The obtained value for the interaction effect of exercise × position, $F = 1.79$ does not exceed the F value of 5.14 in the table at the 0.05 level for d.f. 2 and 6. We therefore accept the null hypothesis and conclude that there is no interaction effect on recovery rate.

Appendix 1

Table of Random Numbers

23157	54859	01837	25993	76249	70886	95230	36744
05545	55043	10537	43508	90611	83744	10962	21343
14871	60350	32404	36223	50051	00322	11543	80834
38976	74951	94051	75853	78805	90194	32428	71695
97312	61718	99755	30870	94251	25841	54882	10513
11742	69381	44339	30872	32797	33118	22647	06850
43361	28859	11016	45623	93009	00499	43640	74036
93806	20478	38268	04491	55751	18932	58475	52571
49540	13181	08429	84187	69538	29661	77738	09527
36768	72633	37948	21569	41959	68670	45274	83880
07092	52392	24627	12067	06558	45344	67338	45320
43310	01081	44863	80307	52555	16148	89742	94647
61570	06360	06173	63775	63148	95123	35017	46993
31352	83799	10779	18941	31579	76448	62584	86919
57048	86526	27795	93692	90529	56546	35065	32254
09243	44200	68721	07137	30729	75756	09298	27650
97957	35018	40894	88329	52230	82521	22532	61587
93732	59570	43781	98885	56671	66826	95996	44569
72621	11225	00922	68264	35666	59434	71687	58167
61020	74418	45371	20794	95917	37866	99536	19378
97839	85474	33055	91718	45473	54144	22034	23000
89160	97192	22232	90637	35055	45489	88438	16361
25966	88220	62871	79265	02823	52862	84919	54883
81443	31719	05049	54806	74690	07567	65017	16543
11322	54931	42362	34386	08624	97687	46245	23245

Appendix 2

χ^2 Distribution

Degrees of freedom	Level of significance	
	0.05	0.01
1	3.84	6.63
2	5.99	9.21
3	7.81	11.34
4	9.49	13.28
5	11.07	15.09
6	12.59	16.81
7	14.07	18.48
8	15.51	20.09
9	16.92	21.67
10	18.31	23.21
11	19.68	24.72
12	21.03	26.22
13	22.36	27.69
14	23.68	29.14
15	25.00	30.58
16	26.30	32.00
17	27.59	33.41
18	28.87	34.81
19	30.14	36.19
20	31.41	37.57
21	32.67	38.93
22	33.92	40.29
23	35.17	41.64
24	36.42	42.98
25	37.65	44.31
26	38.89	45.64
27	40.11	46.96
28	41.34	48.28
29	42.56	49.59
30	43.77	50.89
40	55.76	63.69
50	67.50	76.15
60	79.08	88.38
70	90.53	100.43
80	101.88	112.33
90	113.15	124.12
100	124.34	135.81

Appendix 3

t Distribution

	Level of significance for one-tailed test			
	0.05	0.025	0.01	0.005
	Level of significance for two-tailed test			
d.f.	0.10	0.05	0.02	0.01
1	6.314	12.706	31.821	63.657
2	2.920	4.303	6.965	9.925
3	2.353	3.182	4.541	5.841
4	2.132	2.776	3.747	4.604
5	2.015	2.571	3.365	4.032
6	1.943	2.447	3.143	3.707
7	1.895	2.365	2.998	3.499
8	1.860	2.306	2.896	3.355
9	1.833	2.262	2.821	3.250
10	1.812	2.228	2.764	3.169
11	1.796	2.201	2.718	3.106
12	1.782	2.179	2.681	3.055
13	1.771	2.160	2.650	3.012
14	1.761	2.145	2.624	2.977
15	1.753	2.131	2.602	2.947
16	1.746	2.120	2.583	2.921
17	1.740	2.110	2.567	2.898
18	1.734	2.101	2.552	2.878
19	1.729	2.093	2.539	2.861
20	1.725	2.086	2.528	2.845
21	1.721	2.080	2.518	2.831
22	1.717	2.074	2.508	2.819
23	1.714	2.069	2.500	2.807
24	1.711	2.064	2.492	2.797
25	1.708	2.060	2.485	2.787
26	1.706	2.056	2.479	2.779
27	1.703	2.052	2.473	2.771
28	1.701	2.048	2.467	2.763
29	1.699	2.045	2.462	2.756
30	1.697	2.042	2.457	2.750
40	1.684	2.021	2.423	2.704
60	1.671	2.000	2.390	2.660
120	1.658	1.980	2.358	2.617
∞	1.645	1.960	2.326	2.576

Appendix 4

F Distribution

v_1 = d.f. for the greater variance
v_2 = d.f. for the lesser variance
(a) 0.05 level

v_2 \ v_1	1	2	3	4	5	6	7	8	9
1	161.45	199.50	215.71	224.58	230.16	233.99	236.77	238.88	240.54
2	18.513	19.000	19.164	19.247	19.296	19.330	19.353	19.371	19.385
3	10.128	9.5521	9.2766	9.1172	9.0135	8.9406	8.8867	8.8452	8.8323
4	7.7086	6.9443	6.5914	6.3882	6.2561	6.1631	6.0942	6.0410	5.9938
5	6.6079	5.7861	5.4095	5.1922	5.0503	4.9503	4.8759	4.8183	4.7725
6	5.9874	5.1433	4.7571	4.5337	4.3874	4.2839	4.2067	4.1468	4.0990
7	5.5914	4.7374	4.3468	4.1203	3.9715	3.8660	3.7870	3.7257	3.6767
8	5.3177	4.4590	4.0662	3.8379	3.6875	3.5806	3.5005	3.4381	3.3881
9	5.1174	4.2565	3.8625	3.6331	3.4817	3.3738	3.2927	3.2296	3.1789
10	4.9646	4.1028	3.7083	3.4780	3.3258	3.2172	3.1355	3.0717	3.0204
11	4.8443	3.9823	3.5874	3.3567	3.2039	3.0946	3.0123	2.9480	2.8962
12	4.7472	3.8853	3.4903	3.2592	3.1059	2.9961	2.9134	2.8486	2.7964
13	4.6672	3.8056	3.4105	3.1791	3.0254	2.9153	2.8321	2.7669	2.7444
14	4.6001	3.7389	3.3439	3.1122	2.9582	2.8477	2.7642	2.6987	2.6458
15	4.5431	3.6823	3.2874	3.0556	2.9013	2.7905	2.7066	2.6408	2.5876
16	4.4940	3.6337	3.2389	3.0069	2.8524	2.7413	2.6572	2.5911	2.5377
17	4.4513	3.5915	3.1968	2.9647	2.8100	2.6987	2.6143	2.5480	2.4443
18	4.4139	3.5546	3.1599	2.9277	2.7729	2.6613	2.5767	2.5102	2.4563
19	4.3807	3.5219	3.1274	2.8951	2.7401	2.6283	2.5435	2.4768	2.4227
20	4.3512	3.4928	3.0984	2.8661	2.7109	2.5990	2.5140	2.4471	2.3928
21	4.3248	3.4668	3.0725	2.8401	2.6848	2.5727	2.4876	2.4205	2.3660
22	4.3009	3.4434	3.0491	2.8167	2.6613	2.5491	2.4638	2.3965	2.3219
23	4.2793	3.4221	3.0280	2.7955	2.6400	2.5277	2.4422	2.3748	2.3201
24	4.2597	3.4028	3.0088	2.7763	2.6207	2.5082	2.4226	2.3551	2.3002
25	4.2417	3.3852	2.9912	2.7587	2.6030	2.4904	2.4047	2.3371	2.2821
26	4.2252	3.3690	2.9752	2.7426	2.5868	2.4741	2.3883	2.3205	2.2655
27	4.2100	3.3541	2.9604	2.7278	2.5719	2.4591	2.3732	2.3053	2.2501
28	4.1960	3.3404	2.9467	2.7141	2.5581	2.4453	2.3593	2.2913	2.2360
29	4.1830	3.3277	2.9340	2.7014	2.5454	2.4324	2.3463	2.2783	2.2329
30	4.1709	3.3158	2.9223	2.6896	2.5336	2.4205	2.3343	2.2662	2.2507
40	4.0847	3.2317	2.8387	2.6060	2.4495	2.3359	2.2490	2.1802	2.1240
60	4.0012	3.1504	2.7581	2.5252	2.3683	2.2541	2.1665	2.0970	2.0401
120	3.9201	3.0718	2.6802	2.4472	2.2899	2.1750	2.0868	2.0164	1.9688
∞	3.8415	2.9957	2.6049	2.3719	2.2141	2.0986	2.0096	1.9384	1.8799

F Distribution (continued)

10	12	15	20	24	30	40	60	120	∞
241.88	243.91	245.95	248.01	249.05	250.10	251.14	252.20	253.25	254.31
19.396	19.413	19.429	19.446	19.454	19.462	19.471	19.479	19.487	19.496
8.7855	8.7446	8.7029	8.6602	8.6385	8.6166	8.5944	8.5720	8.5594	8.5264
5.9644	5.9117	5.8578	5.8025	5.7744	5.7459	5.7170	5.6877	5.6381	5.6281
4.7351	4.6777	4.6188	4.5581	4.5272	4.4957	4.4638	4.4314	4.3085	4.3650
4.0600	3.9999	3.9381	3.8742	3.8415	3.8082	3.7743	3.7398	3.7047	3.6689
3.6365	3.5747	3.5107	3.4445	3.4105	3.3758	3.3404	3.3043	3.2674	3.2298
3.3472	3.2839	3.2184	3.1503	3.1152	3.0794	3.0428	3.0053	2.9669	2.9276
3.1373	3.0729	3.0061	2.9365	2.9005	2.8637	2.8259	2.7872	2.7475	2.7067
2.9782	2.9130	2.8450	2.7740	2.7372	2.6996	2.6609	2.6211	2.5801	2.5379
2.8536	2.7876	2.7186	2.6464	2.6090	2.5705	2.5309	2.4901	2.4480	2.4045
2.7534	2.6866	2.6169	2.5436	2.5055	2.4663	2.4259	2.3842	2.3410	2.2962
2.6710	2.6037	2.5331	2.4589	2.4202	2.3803	2.3392	2.2966	2.2524	2.2064
2.6022	2.5342	2.4630	2.3879	2.3487	2.3082	2.2664	2.2229	2.1778	2.1307
2.5437	2.4753	2.4034	2.3275	2.2878	2.2468	2.2043	2.1601	2.1141	2.0658
2.4935	2.4247	2.3522	2.2756	2.2354	2.1938	2.1507	2.1058	2.0589	2.0096
2.4499	2.3807	2.3077	2.2304	2.1898	2.1477	2.1040	2.0584	2.0107	1.9604
2.4117	2.3421	2.2686	2.1906	2.1497	2.1071	2.0629	2.0166	1.9681	1.9168
2.3779	2.3080	2.2341	2.1555	2.1141	2.0712	2.0264	1.9795	1.9302	1.8780
2.3479	2.2776	2.2033	2.1242	2.0825	2.0391	1.9938	1.9464	1.8963	1.8432
2.3210	2.2504	2.1757	2.0960	2.0540	2.0102	1.9645	1.9165	1.8657	1.8117
2.2967	2.2258	2.1508	2.0707	2.0283	1.9842	1.9380	1.8894	1.8380	1.7831
2.2747	2.2036	2.1282	2.0476	2.0050	1.9605	1.9139	1.8648	1.8128	1.7570
2.2547	2.1834	2.1077	2.0267	1.9838	1.9390	1.8920	1.8424	1.7896	1.7330
2.2365	2.1649	2.0889	2.0075	1.9643	1.9192	1.8718	1.8217	1.7684	1.7110
2.2197	2.1479	2.0716	1.9898	1.9464	1.9010	1.8533	1.8027	1.7488	1.6906
2.2043	2.1323	2.0558	1.9736	1.9299	1.8842	1.8361	1.7851	1.7306	1.6717
2.1900	2.1179	2.0411	1.9586	1.9147	1.8687	1.8203	1.7689	1.7138	1.6541
2.1768	2.1045	2.0275	1.9446	1.9005	1.8543	1.8055	1.7537	1.6981	1.6376
2.1646	2.0921	2.0148	1.9317	1.8874	1.8409	1.7918	1.7396	1.6835	1.6223
2.0772	2.0035	1.9245	1.8389	1.7929	1.7444	1.6928	1.6373	1.5766	1.5089
1.9926	1.9174	1.8364	1.7480	1.7001	1.6491	1.5943	1.5343	1.4673	1.3893
1.9105	1.8337	1.7505	1.6587	1.6084	1.5543	1.4952	1.4290	1.3519	1.2539
1.8307	1.7522	1.6664	1.5705	1.5173	1.4591	1.3940	1.3180	1.0214	1.0000

F Distribution
(b)   0.01 level

v_1 $\backslash$ v_2	1	2	3	4	5	6	7	8	9
1	4052.2	4999.5	5403.4	5624.6	5763.6	5859.0	5928.4	5981.1	6022.5
2	98.503	99.000	99.166	99.249	99.299	99.333	99.356	99.374	99.388
3	34.116	30.817	29.457	28.710	28.237	27.911	27.672	27.489	27.345
4	21.198	18.000	16.694	15.977	15.522	15.207	14.976	14.799	14.659
5	16.258	13.274	12.060	11.392	10.967	10.672	10.456	10.289	10.158
6	13.745	10.925	9.7795	9.1483	8.7459	8.4661	8.2600	8.1017	7.9761
7	12.246	9.5466	8.4513	7.8466	7.4604	7.1914	6.9928	6.8400	6.7188
8	11.259	8.6491	7.5910	7.0061	6.6318	6.3707	6.1776	6.0289	5.9106
9	10.561	8.0215	6.9919	6.4221	6.0569	5.8018	5.6129	5.4671	5.3511
10	10.044	7.5594	6.5523	5.9943	5.6363	5.3858	5.2001	5.0567	4.9424
11	9.6460	7.2057	6.2167	5.6683	5.3160	5.0692	4.8861	4.7445	4.6315
12	9.3302	6.9266	5.9525	5.4120	5.0643	4.8206	4.6395	4.4994	4.3875
13	9.0738	6.7010	5.7394	5.2053	4.8616	4.6204	4.4410	4.3021	4.1911
14	8.8616	6.5149	5.5639	5.0354	4.6950	4.4558	4.2779	4.1399	4.0297
15	8.6831	6.3589	5.4170	4.8932	4.5556	4.3183	4.1415	4.0045	3.8948
16	8.5310	6.2262	5.2922	4.7726	4.4374	4.2016	4.0259	3.8896	3.7804
17	8.3997	6.1121	5.1850	4.6690	4.3359	4.1015	3.9267	3.7910	3.6822
18	8.2854	6.0129	5.0919	4.5790	4.2479	4.0146	3.8406	3.7054	3.5971
19	8.1849	5.9259	5.0103	4.5003	4.1708	3.9386	3.7653	3.6305	3.5225
20	8.0960	5.8489	4.9382	4.4307	4.1027	3.8714	3.6987	3.5644	3.4567
21	8.0166	5.7804	4.8740	4.3688	4.0421	3.8117	3.6396	3.5056	3.3981
22	7.9454	5.7190	4.8166	4.3134	3.9880	3.7583	3.5867	3.4530	3.3458
23	7.8811	5.6637	4.7649	4.2636	3.9392	3.7102	3.5390	3.4057	3.2986
24	7.8229	5.6136	4.7181	4.2184	3.8951	3.6667	3.4959	3.3629	3.2560
25	7.7698	5.5680	4.6755	4.1774	3.8550	3.6272	3.4568	3.3239	3.2172
26	7.7213	5.5263	4.6366	4.1400	3.8183	3.5911	3.4210	3.2884	3.1818
27	7.6767	5.4881	4.6009	4.1056	3.7848	3.5580	3.3882	3.2558	3.1494
28	7.6356	5.4529	4.5681	4.0740	3.7539	3.5276	3.3581	3.2259	3.1195
29	7.5977	5.4204	4.5378	4.0449	3.7254	3.4995	3.3303	3.1982	3.0920
30	7.5625	5.3903	4.5097	4.0179	3.6990	3.4735	3.3045	3.1726	3.0665
40	7.3141	5.1785	4.3126	3.8283	3.5138	3.2910	3.1238	2.9930	2.8876
60	7.0771	4.9774	4.1259	3.6490	3.3389	3.1187	2.9530	2.8233	2.7185
120	6.8509	4.7865	3.9491	3.4795	3.1735	2.9559	2.7918	2.6629	2.5586
∞	6.6349	4.6052	3.7816	3.3192	3.0173	2.8020	2.6393	2.5113	2.4073

F Distribution (continued)

10	12	15	20	24	30	40	60	120	∞
6055.8	6106.3	6157.3	6208.7	6234.6	6260.6	6286.8	6313.0	6339.4	6365.9
99.399	99.416	99.433	99.449	99.458	99.466	99.474	99.482	99.491	99.499
27.229	27.052	26.872	26.690	26.598	26.505	26.411	26.316	26.221	26.125
14.546	14.374	14.198	14.020	13.929	13.838	13.745	13.652	13.558	13.463
10.051	9.8883	9.7222	9.5526	9.4665	9.3793	9.2912	9.2020	9.1118	9.0204
7.8741	7.7183	7.5590	7.3958	7.3127	7.2285	7.1432	7.0567	6.9690	6.8800
6.6201	6.4691	6.3143	6.1554	6.0743	5.9920	5.9084	5.8236	5.7373	5.6495
5.8143	5.6667	5.5151	5.3591	5.2793	5.1981	5.1156	5.0316	4.9461	4.8588
5.2565	5.1114	4.9621	4.8080	4.7290	4.6486	4.5666	4.4831	4.3978	4.3105
4.8491	4.7059	4.5581	4.4054	4.3269	4.2469	4.1653	4.0819	3.9965	3.9090
4.5393	4.3974	4.2509	4.0990	4.0209	3.9411	3.8596	3.7761	3.6904	3.6024
4.2961	4.1553	4.0096	3.8584	3.7805	3.7008	3.6192	3.5355	3.4494	3.3608
4.1003	3.9603	3.8154	3.6646	3.5868	3.5070	3.4253	3.3413	3.2548	3.1654
3.9394	3.8001	3.6557	3.5052	3.4274	3.3476	3.2656	3.1813	3.0942	3.0040
3.8049	3.6662	3.5222	3.3719	3.2940	3.2141	3.1319	3.0471	2.9595	2.8684
3.6909	3.5527	3.4089	3.2587	3.1808	3.1007	3.0182	2.9330	2.8447	2.7528
3.5931	3.4552	3.3117	3.1615	3.0835	3.0032	2.9205	2.8348	2.7459	2.6530
3.5082	3.3706	3.2273	3.0771	2.9990	2.9185	2.8354	2.7493	2.6597	2.5660
3.4338	3.2965	3.1533	3.0031	2.9249	2.8442	2.7608	2.6742	2.5839	2.4893
3.3682	3.2311	3.0880	2.9377	2.8594	2.7785	2.6947	2.6077	2.5168	2.4212
3.3098	3.1730	3.0300	2.8796	2.8010	2.7200	2.6359	2.5484	2.4568	2.3603
3.2576	3.1209	2.9779	2.8274	2.7488	2.6675	2.5831	2.4951	2.4029	2.3055
3.2106	3.0740	2.9311	2.7805	2.7017	2.6202	2.5355	2.4471	2.3542	2.2558
3.1681	3.0316	2.8887	2.7380	2.6591	2.5773	2.4923	2.4035	2.3100	2.2107
3.1294	2.9931	2.8502	2.6993	2.6203	2.5383	2.4530	2.3637	2.2696	2.1694
3.0941	2.9578	2.8150	2.6640	2.5848	2.5026	2.4170	2.3273	2.2325	2.1315
3.0618	2.9256	2.7827	2.6316	2.5522	2.4699	2.3840	2.2938	2.1985	2.0965
3.0320	2.8959	2.7530	2.6017	2.5223	2.4397	2.3535	2.2629	2.1670	2.0642
3.0045	2.8685	2.7256	2.5742	2.4946	2.4118	2.3253	2.2344	2.1379	2.0342
2.9791	2.8431	2.7002	2.5487	2.4689	2.3860	2.2992	2.2079	2.1108	2.0062
2.8005	2.6648	2.5216	2.3689	2.2880	2.2034	2.1142	2.0194	1.9172	1.8047
2.6318	2.4961	2.3523	2.1978	2.1154	2.0285	1.9360	1.8363	1.7263	1.6006
2.4721	2.3363	2.1915	2.0346	1.9500	1.8600	1.7628	1.6557	1.5330	1.3805
2.3209	2.1847	2.0385	1.8783	1.7908	1.6964	1.5923	1.4730	1.3246	1.0000

Appendix 5

**Pearson Product Moment Correlation Values at the 0.05 and
0.01 Levels of Significance**

d.f.	0.05	0.01		d.f.	0.05	0.01
1	0.997	0.9999		35	0.325	0.418
2	0.950	0.990		36	0.320	0.413
3	0.878	0.959		38	0.312	0.403
4	0.811	0.917		40	0.304	0.393
5	0.754	0.874		42	0.297	0.384
6	0.707	0.834		44	0.291	0.376
7	0.666	0.798		45	0.288	0.372
8	0.632	0.765		46	0.284	0.368
9	0.602	0.735		48	0.279	0.361
10	0.576	0.708		50	0.273	0.354
11	0.553	0.684		55	0.261	0.338
12	0.532	0.661		60	0.250	0.325
13	0.514	0.641		65	0.241	0.313
14	0.497	0.623		70	0.232	0.302
15	0.482	0.606		75	0.224	0.292
16	0.468	0.590		80	0.217	0.283
17	0.456	0.575		85	0.211	0.275
18	0.444	0.561		90	0.205	0.267
19	0.433	0.549		95	0.200	0.260
20	0.423	0.537		100	0.195	0.254
21	0.413	0.526		125	0.174	0.228
22	0.404	0.515		150	0.159	0.208
23	0.396	0.505		175	0.148	0.193
24	0.388	0.496		200	0.138	0.181
25	0.381	0.487		300	0.113	0.148
26	0.374	0.479		400	0.098	0.128
27	0.367	0.471		500	0.088	0.115
28	0.361	0.463		1,000	0.062	0.081
29	0.355	0.456				
30	0.349	0.449				
32	0.339	0.436				
34	0.329	0.424				

Appendix 6

Spearman Rank Correlation Coefficient Values

	Significance level (one-tailed test)	
N	0.05	0.01
4	1.000	
5	0.900	1.000
6	0.829	0.943
7	0.714	0.893
8	0.643	0.833
9	0.600	0.783
10	0.564	0.746
12	0.506	0.712
14	0.456	0.645
16	0.425	0.601
18	0.399	0.564
20	0.377	0.534
22	0.359	0.508
24	0.343	0.485
26	0.329	0.465
28	0.317	0.448
30	0.306	0.432

Appendix 7

Mann-Whitney U Test Values (Two-Tailed Test)

n_L = larger sample size
n_S = smaller sample size

Two-tailed test, α = 0.05

Rows = n_S (smaller sample), Columns = n_L (larger sample)

n_S \ n_L	2	3	4	5	6	7	8	9	10	11	12	13	14	15	16	17	18	19	20	21	22	23	24	25
2	—	—	—	—	—	—	0	0	0	0	1	1	1	1	1	2	2	2	2	3	3	3	3	3
3	—	—	—	0	1	1	2	2	3	3	4	4	5	5	6	6	7	7	8	8	9	9	10	10
4	—	—	0	1	2	3	4	4	5	6	7	8	9	10	11	11	12	13	14	15	16	17	17	18
5	—	—	—	2	3	5	6	7	8	9	11	12	13	14	15	17	18	19	20	22	23	24	25	27
6	—	—	—	—	5	6	8	10	11	13	14	16	17	19	21	22	24	25	27	29	30	32	33	35
7	—	—	—	—	—	8	10	12	14	16	18	20	22	24	26	28	30	32	34	36	38	40	42	44
8	—	—	—	—	—	—	13	15	17	19	22	24	26	29	31	34	36	38	41	43	45	48	50	53
9	—	—	—	—	—	—	—	17	20	23	26	28	31	34	37	39	42	45	48	50	53	56	59	62
10	—	—	—	—	—	—	—	—	23	26	29	33	36	39	42	45	48	52	55	58	61	64	67	71
11	—	—	—	—	—	—	—	—	—	30	33	37	40	44	47	51	55	58	62	65	69	73	76	80
12	—	—	—	—	—	—	—	—	—	—	37	41	45	49	53	57	61	65	69	73	77	81	85	89
13	—	—	—	—	—	—	—	—	—	—	—	45	50	54	59	63	67	72	76	80	85	89	94	98
14	—	—	—	—	—	—	—	—	—	—	—	—	55	59	64	69	74	78	83	88	93	98	102	107
15	—	—	—	—	—	—	—	—	—	—	—	—	—	64	70	75	80	85	90	96	101	106	111	117
16	—	—	—	—	—	—	—	—	—	—	—	—	—	—	75	81	86	92	98	103	109	115	120	126
17	—	—	—	—	—	—	—	—	—	—	—	—	—	—	—	87	93	99	105	111	117	123	129	135
18	—	—	—	—	—	—	—	—	—	—	—	—	—	—	—	—	99	106	112	119	125	132	138	145
19	—	—	—	—	—	—	—	—	—	—	—	—	—	—	—	—	—	113	119	126	133	140	147	154
20	—	—	—	—	—	—	—	—	—	—	—	—	—	—	—	—	—	—	127	134	141	149	156	163
21	—	—	—	—	—	—	—	—	—	—	—	—	—	—	—	—	—	—	—	142	150	157	165	173
22	—	—	—	—	—	—	—	—	—	—	—	—	—	—	—	—	—	—	—	—	158	166	174	182
23	—	—	—	—	—	—	—	—	—	—	—	—	—	—	—	—	—	—	—	—	—	175	183	192
24	—	—	—	—	—	—	—	—	—	—	—	—	—	—	—	—	—	—	—	—	—	—	192	201
25	—	—	—	—	—	—	—	—	—	—	—	—	—	—	—	—	—	—	—	—	—	—	—	211

Two-tailed test, α = 0.01

n_S \ n_L	2	3	4	5	6	7	8	9	10	11	12	13	14	15	16	17	18	19	20	21	22	23	24	25
2	—	—	—	—	—	—	—	—	—	—	—	—	—	—	—	—	—	—	—	—	—	—	—	—
3	—	—	—	—	—	—	—	0	0	0	1	1	1	2	2	2	2	3	3	3	4	4	4	5
4	—	—	—	—	0	0	1	1	2	2	3	3	4	5	5	6	6	7	8	8	9	9	10	11
5	—	—	—	0	1	1	2	3	4	5	6	7	7	8	9	10	11	12	13	14	15	16	17	18
6	—	—	—	—	2	3	4	5	6	7	9	10	11	12	13	15	16	17	18	19	21	22	23	24
7	—	—	—	—	—	4	6	7	9	10	12	13	15	16	18	19	21	22	24	25	27	28	30	32
8	—	—	—	—	—	—	7	9	11	13	15	17	18	20	22	24	26	28	30	32	34	35	37	39
9	—	—	—	—	—	—	—	11	13	16	18	20	22	24	27	29	31	33	36	38	40	43	45	47
10	—	—	—	—	—	—	—	—	16	18	21	24	26	29	31	34	37	39	42	44	47	50	52	55
11	—	—	—	—	—	—	—	—	—	21	24	27	30	33	36	39	42	45	48	51	54	57	60	63
12	—	—	—	—	—	—	—	—	—	—	27	31	34	37	41	44	47	51	54	58	61	64	68	71
13	—	—	—	—	—	—	—	—	—	—	—	34	38	42	45	49	53	57	60	64	68	72	75	79
14	—	—	—	—	—	—	—	—	—	—	—	—	42	46	50	54	58	63	67	71	75	79	83	87
15	—	—	—	—	—	—	—	—	—	—	—	—	—	51	55	60	64	69	73	78	82	87	91	96
16	—	—	—	—	—	—	—	—	—	—	—	—	—	—	60	65	70	74	79	84	89	94	99	104
17	—	—	—	—	—	—	—	—	—	—	—	—	—	—	—	70	75	81	86	91	96	102	107	112
18	—	—	—	—	—	—	—	—	—	—	—	—	—	—	—	—	81	87	92	98	104	109	115	121
19	—	—	—	—	—	—	—	—	—	—	—	—	—	—	—	—	—	93	99	105	111	117	123	129
20	—	—	—	—	—	—	—	—	—	—	—	—	—	—	—	—	—	—	105	112	118	125	131	138
21	—	—	—	—	—	—	—	—	—	—	—	—	—	—	—	—	—	—	—	118	125	132	139	146
22	—	—	—	—	—	—	—	—	—	—	—	—	—	—	—	—	—	—	—	—	131	140	147	155
23	—	—	—	—	—	—	—	—	—	—	—	—	—	—	—	—	—	—	—	—	—	145	155	163
24	—	—	—	—	—	—	—	—	—	—	—	—	—	—	—	—	—	—	—	—	—	—	160	172
25	—	—	—	—	—	—	—	—	—	—	—	—	—	—	—	—	—	—	—	—	—	—	—	185

Mann-Whitney U Test Values (Two-Tailed Test) (continued)

equal sample sizes

n	1	2	3	4	5	6	7	8	9	10	11	12	13	14	15	16	17	18	19	20	21	22	23	24	25
0.05	–	–	–	0	2	5	8	13	17	23	30	37	45	55	64	75	87	99	113	127	142	158	175	192	211
0.01	–	–	–	–	0	2	4	7	11	16	21	27	34	42	51	60	70	81	93	105	118	133	148	164	180

n	26	27	28	29	30	31	32	33	34	35	36	37	38	39	40	41	42	43	44	45	46	47	48	49	50
0.05	230	250	272	294	317	341	365	391	418	445	473	503	533	564	596	628	662	697	732	769	806	845	884	924	965
0.01	198	216	235	255	276	298	321	344	369	394	420	447	475	504	533	564	595	627	660	694	729	765	802	839	877

Source: Table 5.3, of Neave, H. R., *Statistics Tables*. London: George Allen & Unwin, 1978, p. 53, with the kind permission of the author and publisher.

Appendix 8(a)

Percentage of Scores Under the Normal Curve from 0 to Z									

z	0	1	2	3	4	5	6	7	8	9
0.0	0.0000	0.0040	0.0080	0.0120	0.0160	0.0199	0.0239	0.0279	0.0319	0.0359
0.1	0.0198	0.0438	0.0478	0.0517	0.0557	0.0596	0.0636	0.0675	0.0714	0.0754
0.2	0.0793	0.0832	0.0871	0.0910	0.0948	0.0987	0.1026	0.1064	0.1103	0.1141
0.3	0.1179	0.1217	0.1255	0.1293	0.1331	0.1368	0.1406	0.1443	0.1480	0.1517
0.4	0.1554	0.1591	0.1628	0.1664	0.1700	0.1736	0.1772	0.1808	0.1844	0.1879
0.5	0.1915	0.1950	0.1985	0.2019	0.2054	0.2088	0.2123	0.2157	0.2190	0.2224
0.6	0.2258	0.2291	0.2324	0.2357	0.2389	0.2422	0.2454	0.2486	0.2518	0.2549
0.7	0.2580	0.2612	0.2642	0.2673	0.2704	0.2734	0.2764	0.2794	0.2823	0.2852
0.8	0.2881	0.2910	0.2939	0.2967	0.2996	0.3023	0.3051	0.3078	0.3106	0.3133
0.9	0.3159	0.3180	0.3212	0.3238	0.3264	0.3289	0.3315	0.3340	0.3365	0.3389
1.0	0.3413	0.3438	0.3461	0.3485	0.3508	0.3531	0.3554	0.3577	0.3599	0.3621
1.1	0.3643	0.3665	0.3686	0.3708	0.3729	0.3749	0.3770	0.3790	0.3810	0.3830
1.2	0.3849	0.3869	0.3888	0.3907	0.3925	0.3944	0.3962	0.3980	0.3997	0.4015
1.3	0.4032	0.4049	0.4066	0.4082	0.4099	0.4115	0.4131	0.4147	0.4162	0.4177
1.4	0.4192	0.4207	0.4222	0.4236	0.4251	0.4265	0.4279	0.4292	0.4306	0.4319
1.5	0.4332	0.4345	0.4357	0.4370	0.4382	0.4394	0.4406	0.4418	0.4429	0.4441
1.6	0.4452	0.4463	0.4474	0.4484	0.4495	0.4505	0.4515	0.4525	0.4535	0.4545
1.7	0.4554	0.4564	0.4573	0.4582	0.4591	0.4599	0.4608	0.4616	0.4625	0.4633
1.8	0.4641	0.4649	0.4656	0.4664	0.4671	0.4678	0.4686	0.4693	0.4699	0.4706
1.9	0.4713	0.4719	0.4726	0.4732	0.4738	0.4744	0.4750	0.4756	0.4761	0.4767

Percentage of Scores Under the Normal Curve from 0 to Z (continued)

z	0	1	2	3	4	5	6	7	8	9
2.0	0.4772	0.4778	0.4783	0.4788	0.4793	0.4798	0.4803	0.4808	0.4812	0.4817
2.1	0.4821	0.4826	0.4830	0.4834	0.4838	0.4842	0.4846	0.4850	0.4854	0.4857
2.2	0.4861	0.4864	0.4868	0.4871	0.4875	0.4878	0.4881	0.4884	0.4887	0.4890
2.3	0.4893	0.4896	0.4898	0.4901	0.4904	0.4906	0.4909	0.4911	0.4913	0.4916
2.4	0.4918	0.4920	0.4922	0.4925	0.4927	0.4929	0.4931	0.4932	0.4934	0.4936
2.5	0.4938	0.4940	0.4941	0.4943	0.4945	0.4946	0.4948	0.4949	0.4951	0.4952
2.6	0.4953	0.4955	0.4956	0.4957	0.4959	0.4960	0.4961	0.4962	0.4963	0.4964
2.7	0.4965	0.4966	0.4967	0.4968	0.4969	0.4970	0.4971	0.4972	0.4973	0.4974
2.8	0.4974	0.4975	0.4976	0.4977	0.4977	0.4978	0.4979	0.499	0.4980	0.4981
2.9	0.4981	0.4982	0.4982	0.4983	0.4984	0.4984	0.4985	0.4985	0.4986	0.4986
3.0	0.4987	0.4987	0.4987	0.4988	0.4988	0.4989	0.4989	0.4989	0.4990	0.4990
3.1	0.4990	0.4991	0.4991	0.4991	0.4992	0.4992	0.4992	0.4992	0.4993	0.4993
3.2	0.4993	0.4993	0.4994	0.4994	0.4994	0.4994	0.4994	0.4995	0.4995	0.4995
3.3	0.4995	0.4995	0.4995	0.4996	0.4996	0.4996	0.4996	0.4996	0.4996	0.4997
3.4	0.4997	0.4997	0.4997	0.4997	0.4997	0.4997	0.4997	0.4997	0.4997	0.4998
3.5	0.4998	0.4998	0.4998	0.4998	0.4998	0.4998	0.4998	0.4998	0.4998	0.4999
3.6	0.4998	0.4999	0.4999	0.4999	0.4999	0.4999	0.4999	0.4999	0.4999	0.4999
3.7	0.4999	0.4999	0.4999	0.4999	0.4999	0.4999	0.4999	0.4999	0.4999	0.4999
3.8	0.4999	0.4999	0.4999	0.4999	0.4999	0.4999	0.4999	0.4999	0.4999	0.4999
3.9	0.5000	0.5000	0.5000	0.5000	0.5000	0.5000	0.5000	0.5000	0.5000	0.5000

Appendix 8(b)

Probabilities Associated with Values as Extreme as
Observed Value of Z in the Normal Curve
of Distribution

z	0.00	0.01	0.02	0.03	0.04	0.05	0.06	0.07	0.08	0.09
0.0	0.5000	0.4960	0.4920	0.4880	0.4840	0.4801	0.4761	0.4721	0.4681	0.4641
0.1	0.4602	0.4562	0.4522	0.4480	0.4413	0.4404	0.4364	0.4325	0.4286	0.4247
0.2	0.4207	0.4168	0.4129	0.4090	0.4052	0.4013	0.3974	0.3936	0.3897	0.3859
0.3	0.3821	0.3783	0.3745	0.3707	0.3669	0.3632	0.3594	0.3557	0.3520	0.3483
0.4	0.3446	0.3409	0.3372	0.3336	0.3300	0.3264	0.3228	0.3192	0.3156	0.3121
0.5	0.3085	0.3050	0.3015	0.2981	0.2946	0.2912	0.2877	0.2843	0.2810	0.2776
0.6	0.2743	0.2709	0.2676	0.2643	0.2611	0.2578	0.2546	0.2514	0.2483	0.2451
0.7	0.2420	0.2389	0.2358	0.2327	0.2296	0.2266	0.2236	0.2206	0.2177	0.2148
0.8	0.2119	0.2090	0.2061	0.2033	0.2005	0.1977	0.1949	0.1922	0.1894	0.1867
0.9	0.1841	0.1814	0.1788	0.1762	0.1736	0.1711	0.1685	0.1660	0.1635	0.1611
1.0	0.1587	0.1562	0.1539	0.1515	0.1492	0.1469	0.1446	0.1423	0.1401	0.1379
1.1	0.1357	0.1335	0.1314	0.1292	0.1271	0.1251	0.1230	0.1210	0.1190	0.1170
1.2	0.1151	0.1131	0.1112	0.1093	0.1075	0.1056	0.1038	0.1020	0.1003	0.0985
1.3	0.0968	0.0951	0.0934	0.0918	0.0901	0.0885	0.0869	0.0853	0.0838	0.0823
1.4	0.0808	0.0793	0.0778	0.0761	0.0749	0.0735	0.0721	0.0708	0.0694	0.0681
1.5	0.0668	0.0655	0.0643	0.0630	0.0618	0.0606	0.0594	0.0582	0.0571	0.0559
1.6	0.0548	0.0537	0.0526	0.0516	0.0505	0.0495	0.0485	0.0475	0.0465	0.0455
1.7	0.0446	0.0436	0.0427	0.0418	0.0409	0.0401	0.0392	0.0384	0.0375	0.0367
1.8	0.0359	0.0351	0.0344	0.0336	0.0329	0.0322	0.0314	0.0307	0.0301	0.0294
1.9	0.0287	0.0281	0.0274	0.0268	0.0262	0.0256	0.0250	0.0244	0.0239	0.0233

Read values of z to one decimal place down the left hand column *Column z*.
Read across *Row z* for values to two decimal places. The probabilities contained
in the table are *one-tailed*. For two-tailed tests, multiply by 2.

Probabilities Associated with Values as Extreme as Observed Value of Z in the Normal Curve of Distribution (continued)

z	0.00	0.01	0.02	0.03	0.04	0.05	0.06	0.07	0.08	0.09
2.0	0.0228	0.0222	0.0217	0.0212	0.0207	0.0202	0.0197	0.0192	0.0188	0.0183
2.1	0.0179	0.0174	0.0170	0.0166	0.0162	0.0158	0.0154	0.0150	0.0146	0.0143
2.2	0.0139	0.0136	0.0132	0.0129	0.0125	0.0122	0.0119	0.0116	0.0113	0.0110
2.3	0.0107	0.0101	0.0102	0.0099	0.0096	0.0094	0.0094	0.0089	0.0087	0.0084
2.4	0.0082	0.0080	0.0078	0.0075	0.0073	0.0071	0.0069	0.0068	0.0066	0.0064
2.5	0.0062	0.0060	0.0059	0.0057	0.0055	0.0054	0.0052	0.0051	0.0049	0.0048
2.6	0.0047	0.0045	0.0044	0.0043	0.0041	0.0040	0.0039	0.0038	0.0037	0.0036
2.7	0.0035	0.0034	0.0033	0.0032	0.0031	0.0030	0.0029	0.0028	0.0027	0.0026
2.8	0.0026	0.0025	0.0024	0.0023	0.0023	0.0022	0.0021	0.0021	0.0020	0.0019
2.9	0.0019	0.0018	0.0018	0.0017	0.0016	0.0016	0.0015	0.0015	0.0014	0.0014
3.0	0.0013	0.0013	0.0013	0.0012	0.0012	0.0011	0.0011	0.0011	0.0010	0.0010
3.1	0.0010	0.0009	0.0009	0.0009	0.0008	0.0008	0.0008	0.0008	0.0007	0.0007
3.2	0.0007									
3.3	0.0005									
3.4	0.0003									
3.5	0.00023									
3.6	0.00016									
3.7	0.00011									
3.8	0.00007									
3.9	0.00005									
4.0	0.00003									

Examples

(i) The probability of a $z \geq 0.14$ on a one-tailed test is $p = 0.4443$

(ii) The probability of a $z \geq 1.98$ on a two-tailed test is $p = 2 \times (0.0239) = 0.0478$

Bibliography

H. M. Blalock, Jnr., *Social Statistics*. New York: McGraw-Hill, 1960

N. J. Conover, *Practical Nonparametric Statistics*. New York: John Wiley and Sons Inc., 1971

C. O. Dotson and D. R. Kirkendall, *Statistics for Physical Education, Health and Recreation*. New York: Harper and Row, 1974

A. L. Edwards, *Statistical Analysis*. New York: Holt, Rinehart and Winston, 1958

B. F. Everitt, *The Analysis of Contingency Tables*. London, Chapman and Hall, 1977

H. E. Garrett, *Statistics in Psychology and Education*. London: Longman, 1966

E. S. Gellman, *Statistics for Teachers*. New York: Harper and Row, 1973

J. D. Gibbons, *Nonparametric Methods for Quantitative Analysis*. New York: Holt, Rinehart and Winston, 1976

M. Hamburg, *Basic Statistics: A Modern Approach*. New York: Harcourt, Brace Jovanovitch, 1974

F. N. Kerlinger, *Foundations of Behavioural Research*. London: Holt, Rinehart and Winston, 1973

D. G. Lewis, *Experimental Design in Education*. London: University of London Press, 1968

R. B. McCall, *Fundamental Statistics for Psychology*. New York: Harcourt, Brace and World, 1970

R. Meddis, *Statistical Handbook for Non-Statisticians*. London: McGraw-Hill, 1975

H. R. Neave, *Statistics Tables*. London: George Allen & Unwin, 1978

The Open University, *Education Course E 341*. Open Univ. Press, Walton Hall, Milton Keynes

W. J. Popham and K. A. Sirotnik, *Educational Statistics*. New York: Harper and Row, 1973

C. Robson, *Experiment, Design and Statistics in Psychology*. London: Penguin, 1973

S. Seigel, *Nonparametric Statistics for the Behavioural Sciences*. New York: McGraw-Hill, 1956

J. C. Weber and D. R. Lamb, *Statistics and Research in Physical Education*. St. Louis: C. V. Mosby, 1970

B. J. Winer, *Statistical Principles in Experimental Design*. New York: McGraw-Hill, 1971

Index